R. H. Wills.

H. N. C.

THE PROCESS OF HUMAN BEHAVIOR

THE PROCESS OF
HUMAN BEHAVIOR

By MANDEL SHERMAN, M.D., Ph.D.
and IRENE CASE SHERMAN, Ph.D.

LONDON
WILLIAMS AND NORGATE LTD.
38 GREAT ORMOND STREET

PRINTED IN THE U. S. A. PUBLISHED 1930

Contents

5

List of Illustrations

PREFACE

The experimental work upon which this book is based was begun in 1923 at the Lying-In Hospital in Chicago, where studies of the sensori-motor activities of infants were conducted jointly by the authors. This material is presented in Chapters III and IV. In 1925 further experiments were started by Dr. Mandel Sherman at the Wesley Memorial Hospital, Chicago, and in the Neuro-Psychiatric Clinic of Northwestern University Medical School, the major part of this work including a study of the differentiation of emotions in infants, the results of which are given in Chapters V and VI. In Chapters I and II on the Nervous System much has been borrowed from other authors. Chapters VII and VIII on Personality have been prepared jointly, and the system as a whole represents a point of view shared by both authors.

During the past year experimental work and clinical experience at the Washington Child Research Center have furnished the opportunity to compare the reactions of infants with older children in the Nursery School section for normal children and in the Behavior Clinic for children of all ages.

The pioneer experimental investigations of John B. Watson on the emotions of infants provided the stimulus for the work on emotional responses reported in this volume. Grateful acknowledgment is made for the use of some of his methods of initiating such responses.

The authors are indebted to the editor of the Journal of Comparative Psychology, published by the Williams and Wilkins Company, the Journal of Abnormal and Social Psychology and the Illinois Medical Journal for permission to make use of material previously published by them. They also wish to acknowledge the permission granted by Columbia University Contributions to Education and Henry Holt and Company to reproduce a table and two figures.

INTRODUCTION

This book does not attempt to present an exhaustive study of its subject. Its aim is rather to outline the principles underlying the processes of human behavior and the important factors which influence it; to describe the working of the human organism as a whole, and the genesis and development of the methods by which adjustments of the individual to his environment are effected. Academic physiology, psychology, and neurology (except for a brief description of the human nervous system) have accordingly been omitted, for details of the structure and function of the various sensory and motor organs are best left to analysis by the anatomists, and the reader who requires such information should refer to special books dealing with these subjects. As much can be learned concerning the origin and development of human processes by a study of the varied and increasingly adaptive behavior of animals as it occurs at successive stages of advance in the phylogenetic scale, a rapid survey of such behavior has first been made, including a brief outline of the development of the nervous system and its rôle in the integration of sensory and motor end organs. Throughout the book experimental data have been presented in order to make clear the discussion of the various principles outlined.

The doctrines of the various "schools" of psychology—of the "Introspectionists," "Structuralists," "Gestaltists," "Behaviorists," and so on—have not been included because we believe that such doctrines are not a part of the factual matter of the science of behavior, but rightfully belong to philosophy. The psychologist and the psychiatrist are concerned with understanding human behavior and with the possibilities of determining cause and effect relationships between various environmental factors and the action of the individual. For this reason their primary concern is with the adjustment of the individual in his social situations. But they must approach their problems from the experimental rather than the interpretative standpoint. An objective and biological approach to the study of human behavior is imperative for an understanding of the methods by which the individual gains control over his environment. Man is one of the organisms in the evolutionary scale and can be studied, like any other organism, in the biological laboratory.

For a long time the human infant was regarded as too precious for laboratory experiment and many assumptions were made concerning the existence of inherited characteristics, instincts, tendencies, and so on. In recent years, however, controlled observations of infants have been revealing that the human individual is born with very little in the way of perfected types of reaction; that the behavior of the child and adult for the most part develops out of the diffuse, undifferentiated activities of the newborn; and that the adult owes the great variability of his responses to their origin as aimless and chaotic reactions which, through training and experience, become coördinated into socially valuable behavior. It is with this work and its implications for human behavior that the present volume deals.

THE PROCESS OF HUMAN BEHAVIOR

Chapter I

THE GROWTH AND IMPORTANCE OF THE NERVOUS SYSTEM IN ANIMALS AND MAN

THE BEGINNING OF BEHAVIOR IN THE ONE-CELLED ANIMALS

THE development of intelligence and varied behavior depends upon the existence of a nervous system which makes it possible to react in a number of ways to a specific condition. This power of varied response becomes progressively greater as the nervous system develops, and enables an impulse which starts in a single sense organ to reach the motor nerves of a great number of muscles, thus making possible a great number of reactions.

A one-celled animal such as an amoeba or a paramecium, which has no nervous apparatus, can react in only one of two ways to external conditions, namely, by going toward or retreating from the stimulating circumstance. The amoeba, which is the least developed of these one-celled animals, possesses no differentiating structures, each part of the organism functioning in a manner similar to all other parts; that is, the protoplasm of these animals is almost uniform and every part may do many things—receive stimuli, conduct them from one part of the animal to the other, make movements, and so on. The absence of a special nervous system to connect the various parts of the animal results in a stereotyped method of activity. The unicellular animal is able, however, to modify its behavior to a limited extent by adjustment to external stimuli. For example, when it receives a harmful stimulus it changes the shape of its protoplasm and quickly moves away. Adjustment to an external stimulus, then, does not depend wholly upon a nervous system, but the lack of nervous structure does result in a limited and stereotyped manner of behavior.

THE FIRST APPEARANCE OF A STRUCTURE WHICH MAKES THE BEHAVIOR OF ANIMALS MORE VARIED

The first differentiating mechanism which the unicellular animal develops is the *flagellum*. By means of the flagella, long thin filaments situated at one of its ends, the organism attains a definite polarity, that is, it now assumes a definite position in relation to its environment; instead of having no definite anterior or posterior end as in the case of the amoeba, it now develops an anterior or head portion as distinct from the rest of the body. As a result it moves in a definite direction in relation to its body, that is, it always moves forward with the head end, or flagella, first. In addition, its sensory acuity becomes greater because these filamentous structures, which are more sensitive

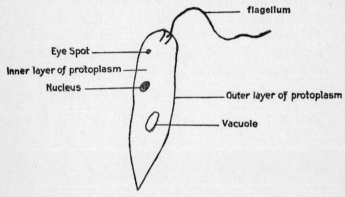

Fig. 1. A flagellated unicellular animal.

than the rest of the body, come in contact with environmental stimuli before the body reaches them. Thus there develops a difference in the function of the anterior and posterior ends of the organism, a difference which, although very slight in these flagellated unicellular organisms, becomes increasingly greater in the course of phylogenetic development.

The filamentous flagella which project at one end of the animal's body do not, however, cause any important differentiation in function or permanently modify the behavior of the animal.

The hair-like *cilia,* which appear in somewhat higher animals, are probably the first signs of a definite differentiation in structure and function of the different parts of the body. They are usually active primarily as motor organs. By a waving motion they produce a current in the water in which the animal lives which helps to sweep food particles into the mouth. Cilia also act as special sensory organs and though they do not contain any nerve elements they are very sensitive to external stimuli and play an important part in initiating movements which are quickly transferred to other parts of the animal.

THE APPEARANCE OF NERVES AND THEIR COMBINATION INTO A NERVE NET

The jelly fish is often cited as one of the first animals to develop a true nervous system. It possesses a network of nerves, that is, a nervous system composed of nerve cells and their extensions, connected loosely into a network. One can readily understand the importance of this change in the structure of an animal. The network of nerves allows for a quick reception of stimuli and also for the immediate transmission of impulses to various parts of the body in a much more rapid and somewhat more definite form than is possible in the one-celled animals. The transmission of impulses in this type of nervous system is much more diffuse, however, than in the nervous systems of animals in which the nerve cells are arranged in central locations.   In the nerve net arrange-

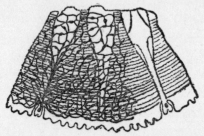

Fig. 2.   A nerve net, showing nerve cells and their diffuse connections.   (From Herrick, after Bethe.)

ment an impulse may spread to any part of the body and may travel in any direction.

Change in Behavior due to the Nerve Net

Despite the fact that impulses are transmitted in a diffuse manner through the nerve net, animals possessing this arrangement react in a much more specific manner than those possessing no nervous structure.   The nerve net allows: first, a quicker reaction; second, a more definite response to a stimulus than is possible when the entire body of the animal acts as the conductor of impulses; third, more complex reactions because an impulse can travel to many parts of the body.   The progress of an animal in adapting itself to its environment depends a great deal upon the number of reactions it can make and its ability to combine these responses into adaptive acts.

Thus we see that as the nervous structure develops the animal is able to make reactions which allow it to adjust to its environment in a more adequate manner. In one-celled animals, such as the amoeba which possesses not even the beginnings of nervous tissue, the reactions are stereotyped and the types of responses limited. The development of cilia allows for a quicker and more accurate detection of stimuli and, therefore, enables the animal to respond more adequately. The adaptive reactions are further developed in animals which possess nerve cells, and the combination of nerve cells into a nerve net marks the beginning of the highly adaptive and coördinated activity noted in the higher animals. The nerve net, therefore, may be spoken of as the rudiment of the central nervous system.

CENTRALIZATION OF THE NERVOUS SYSTEM

The development of a nerve net is the first definite step in the process of *centralization* of animal activities. For the first time in the evolution of organisms the various motor and sensory parts of the body are definitely connected with each other. This close relationship between sensory and motor structures, though vastly superior to the organization of the one-celled animals is, however, still very inferior to that of higher organisms in which the nerve cells are actually centralized and where specific nerve paths are established. In the nerve net any impulse may be transmitted in all directions, and the activity of this type of organism is much more general than that of the higher animals. The reader may infer that the responses of the nerve net type of animal are always diffuse; actually, however, many of its responses are quite specific.

This increased efficiency in adaptive activities is due not only to the more efficient transmission of impulses, but also to greater sensitiveness of the receptive organs. One of the important functions of any nerve arrangement is that of making one part of the body more sensitive than another, and this increased sensitivity in certain regions of the body is an important step in the growth of the centralization process. It is strikingly illustrated in the case of the mouth region. As animals develop in the phylogenetic scale, the head or mouth end develops increasingly greater sensitivity in relation to the other parts of the body, a condition which also holds in human beings.

Cephalization

By *cephalization* is meant the grouping of the important nerve structures in the head end of the body and the resulting dominance of this end over the other parts. The beginning of this dominance is seen in animals as low in the scale as the flagellated one-celled organisms where, although there is no marked differentiation of the various parts, nevertheless the head end reacts to stimuli more specifically than other parts of the body. As nerve cells and nerve structures in general develop, the dominance of the anterior end of the body becomes increasingly greater. The mouth end becomes definitely more sensitive even where specific nerve elements do not yet exist, as in the functional arrangement of the starfish and sponges. The importance of this dominance in the adaptive activities of organisms cannot be overemphasized. The greater sensitiveness of the head end introduces a polarization of the body and makes for a differentiation in the function of its various parts.

THE DEVELOPMENT OF A CENTRAL NERVOUS SYSTEM

The central nervous system develops soon after the nerve net in the phylogenetic scale. In the nerve net appear the three important elements of human organization, namely, the receptor or sensory organ, the effector or motor organ, and the connecting or correlating mechanism. The change from the nerve net to the central nervous system first appears in the head end of the organism. The first animal to show this change is the flat worm in which a ring of nervous tissue develops around the pharynx, with ganglia or groups of nerve cells on either side.

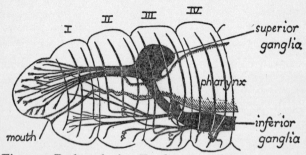

Fig. 3. Brain of the Earthworm. (From Herrick, modified from Shipley and MacBride.)

In the annelides, worms above the flat worm in the evolutionary scale, the nervous system is arranged in a segmental form, that is, a pair of ganglia for each segment of the body. Each pair of ganglia locally controls the segment to which it is attached, but in addition there are now connecting fibers between each pair of ganglia. These connecting fibers are important in correlating the activity of the various parts of the body.

The central nervous system of the higher worms shows a further advance towards both centralization and cephalization by the definite formation of a brain through fusion of the head ganglia into two large masses of nerve cells appearing as enlargements above and below the mouth. The nervous system of these invertebrates is ventral, that is, it lies below the body cavities, and the formation of a ganglion above the esophagus is the first indication of the dorsal position (i. e. above the body cavities) which, as we shall see, the nervous system occupies in the highest animals. The responses of these higher worms are controlled to a great extent by the brain, although there is considerable autonomy in the ganglia of the various segments.

The Synaptic Nervous System

There are in general two differences between the nervous system of the nerve net type as in the jelly fish and that of animals higher in the evolutionary scale which account for the better adaptability of the latter. The first difference is in the transmission of nerve impulses over a synaptic space; the second is the arrangement of the nerve cells into groups or ganglia which in turn form masses making up the central nervous system. These two differences really develop simultaneously in the evolutionary scale. We have seen that the nerve net is made up of the filaments of the nerve cells connecting with each other into a net arrangement, that in consequence impulses aroused by any stimulus may travel in all directions, no one part of the body being favored, and that the resulting activity is diffuse compared with that of the higher animals. The synaptic nervous system differs from the nerve net type in that the ends of the filaments are separated from each other by an extremely small space. The nerve cells now are not directly connected and nervous impulses must overcome a certain amount of resistance in passing this space which is called the *synapse*.

The synapse introduces an additional significant factor in the behavior of animals. The resistance of one group of synapses may be lowered or heightened and impulses from certain stimuli may, therefore, favor one pathway or another. The lowering of the resistance in certain directions allows for the establishment of definite pathways for impulses from various stimuli. The establishment of such definite pathways in the nervous system accounts for the development of definite modes of activity in response to definite stimuli, that is, for the forming of *habits*. Let us emphasize here, as we shall again later, that the adaptability of an organism depends upon the number of habits which it is capable of forming.

The functions of the synapse, then, appear to be twofold: first, to increase the resistance to the impulse; and second, to allow the impulse to travel in only one direction. This polarization of the impulse, that is, its inability to pass in the reverse direction, is also an important factor in the establishment of definite pathways. In the nerve net type of nervous system where impulses may travel in any direction no precise pathways are established. In the synaptic nervous system the irreversibility of conduction at the synapse helps to maintain and make definite the pathways formed by the lowering of the resistance to impulses from definite stimuli.

The Adaptive Possibilities of Animals Possessing a Central Nervous System

The development of a central nervous system in which nerve cells are localized into groups or ganglia is an important step in the evolution of the human brain. We have seen that in the phylogenetic growth of the nervous system cephalization results in the dominance of the head end over other parts of the body. The sensory apparatus of the head becomes more specialized, and the response to stimulation of the head end of an organism is more significant for it than the reactions of other parts of the body. Grouping of cells also allows for a more precise correlation in the nervous system. Impulses from the sensory nerves may be directly and precisely transferred to the appropriate motor nerves with the least possible loss of energy. The arrangement of nerve cells into centrally located groups also makes possible the transmission of impulses from the sensory nerves into more than one pathway so that a number of muscles may be innervated as the result of one stimulus, thus providing a more complicated and more adaptive type of response. The efficiency of the brain of higher animals and of man depends to a great extent upon the number of association cells and pathways which make possible a highly correlated activity of the sensory and motor elements of the nervous system.

The centralized nervous system, then, shows the following increased possibilities for adaptation: (1) the development of a more distinct type of activity; (2) more precise responses to external stimuli; (3) increased coördination between the various segments of the body; (4) more definite polarization with a constant head end and tail; (5) dominance or control of the rest of the body by the ganglia in the head end; (6) formation of acts which may be termed true habits.

The Growth of the Nervous System

The centralization reached in the nervous system of the higher worms is only primitive compared to that of the vertebrates, animals with a vertebral column and either a cartilaginous or a bony skeleton. The various ganglia of the invertebrates function independently to some extent; the interdependence of ganglia and the domination of the brain over the entire body develop later, in the vertebrates, which accordingly possess a more highly correlated nervous system with greater cephalization.

Centralization in the vertebrates shows a further advance in that the segmental ganglia and their processes move closer together and are arranged into one continuous spinal cord. This allows for a close interrelationship between the various nerve cells. The nervous system is now removed from the ventral position it occupies in the invertebrates, where it is in danger of injury, to the dorsal position where it is further protected by the skeletal structure within which it lies.

THE DIFFERENTIATION OF THE NERVOUS SYSTEM INTO SENSORY AND MOTOR PARTS

When both the sensory and motor cells of the nervous system are centrally located differentiation of the receptor endings of the sensory cells occurs and this differentiation is seen in a highly specialized form in the vertebrates. The various nerve endings in the skin are modified to form touch, temperature, pressure and other receptors. The special sense organs, such as those of vision, taste, and hearing, are also clearly differentiated. In the invertebrates the sensory cells are found in the skin or just beneath it, but in the vertebrates these cells assume a specific position, grouped into ganglia placed dorsally just outside of the spinal cord and brain. These ganglia form the sensory roots of the peripheral nerves, and are connected with the motor areas of the central nervous system within the spinal cord and brain by means of relatively short processes. The cells of the motor divisions of the peripheral nerves are also arranged in groups placed in a ventral position within the central nervous system. Because of the complexity of the brain due to its many divisions, proliferations and folds, these relative positions of the sensory and motor nerve cells are not as strictly maintained as in the spinal cord.

The vertebrates, possessing special end organs, are sensitive to more varied stimuli than lower animals, and their adaptive reactions are therefore more specific. Their ability to react to a large number of stimuli because of these specialized sense organs gives them a mode of behavior which is distinctly more complex than that found in simpler forms.   The range of these stimuli increases with the phylogenetic development of the nervous system, resulting in an increasing ability to adapt to a more complex environment.

THE CEREBRAL CORTEX

For practical purposes the *cortex,* or outer layer of the cerebral hemispheres, is divided into the frontal, parietal, temporal, and occipital lobes. The lobes are symmetrically placed, that is, they lie in corresponding positions in the two hemispheres. The hemispheres are divided by a longitudinal fissure and are connected with each other at the bottom of this fissure by three bands of association neurons. The various lobes are separated from each other by smaller fissures called *sulci,* the most important of which are the *lateral sulcus* (the fissure of Sylvius) at the top of the temporal lobe, and the *central sulcus* (fissure of Rolando) between the frontal and parietal lobes.

Immediately in front of the central sulcus, in the posterior portion of the frontal lobes, lies the area from which *motor impulses* are projected. These impulses reach a part of the body opposite the side on which they are initiated, the nerve fibers crossing to the opposite side of the spinal cord in their descent.   The motor projection area may be divided into fairly definite regions although experimental observation has shown that there is no exact point for point localization here. The uppermost part of this area controls the movements of the lower part of the body, and the lower end controls those of the head, face and neck.

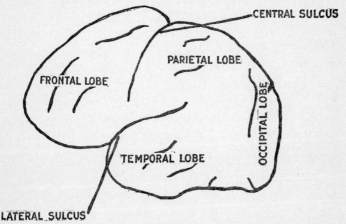

Fig. 4.   Diagram of the left cerebral hemisphere of the adult human brain.

Immediately behind the central sulcus is the somaesthetic area which receives the sensory impulses from the muscles, joints, tendons, and skin. The functional and structural divisions of the *somaesthetic area* are similar to those of the motor area.   The center for vision is located in the occipital lobe, and the auditory center in the upper part of the temporal lobe.   The center for olfaction is in a part of the cortex called the hippocampus, which is infolded so that it is not visible on the surface of the brain. These various centers occupy a relatively small portion of the cortex, the greater part of which is made up of *association centers,* whose function is to connect the sensory and motor areas. They are not distinctly circumscribed for they radiate to such an extent that they cannot be exactly defined. This is especially true of the motor and somaesthetic areas; although the general functions of the two may be differentiated, experimental evidence shows that their boundaries overlap. It is possible that the two are so closely linked by association fibers that they cannot be distinctly separated.

No attempt will be made to discuss the question of the existence of special centers for various mental functions. Although early investigators attempted to ascribe certain mental functions to particular areas in the cerebral cortex, recent investigators have failed to substantiate their claims. Postmortem examinations of abnormal conditions in man and the operative removal of definite areas of the brain of animals have given ample evidence that the cerebral cortex acts as a whole. It has been shown, for example, that experimental lesions which destroy a relatively large part of the cortex often have but little influence upon the behavior of the animal. Observation of persons with abnormal cerebral conditions has also shown that the symptoms do not always depend upon the particular part affected.

The Growth of Animals in the Evolutionary Scale Correlated with the Increasing Development of the Cortex

The development of the brain is perhaps influenced more by the development of the sensory elements than by any other single factor. As the various end organs for sensitivity are developed corresponding areas in the central nervous system appear. For example, the area for smell which forms the greater part of the hemispheres in fishes is relatively extremely small in man. The sense of smell is important to the fish in its adaptation to the environment in which it lives, its function being mainly to detect food. In the adaptive behavior of man, on the other hand, smell is relatively unimportant and the area for olfaction in the human brain is small.

Similarly, other areas change in size, position and dominance in proportion to the importance of the particular sense data they represent in the adjustment of the particular organism to its environment. A good example of this is seen in the development in the mammal of the sensory area which receives impulses from the skin and muscles. The mammal is obviously more dependent upon varied sense data originating in the skin than is the fish which lives in a fairly homogeneous medium. Furthermore, the mammal, with rare exceptions, lives upon land and depends upon sense data from its muscles and skeleton to a much greater extent than the fish. Accordingly the corresponding area in the cortex develops in the mammal and assumes an extremely important function in its adaptive reactions.

Increasing evolutionary development in the animal world is accompanied by the progressive increase in the association areas of the cortex and the relative decrease in the size of the sensory centers. The cortex of the lower vertebrates is composed mainly of sensory and motor centers and contains relatively few association cells to connect the various areas. The relative decrease in the size of the sensory centers does not mean, however, a decrease in the importance of these areas. As a matter of fact, man, the visual centers in whose brain are relatively small, is more receptive to visual sense data than many of the animals whose visual centers form the predominant cortical area. The various centers such as smell, vision, and hearing, assume separate positions and are dominated in extent by the growing association areas of the cerebral hemispheres. The significance of the cortex for complex behavior is indicated by its relative weight in the brain of man where it equals approximately sixty to seventy percent of the weight of the hemispheres.

The development of the various sensory end organs and the increasing range of stimuli to which organisms must adjust as they advance in the evolutionary scale bring about other important changes in the structure of the brain. One of the most significant is the development of a more direct relationship between the motor and sensory cortical areas. As previously mentioned, the sensory areas in the brain develop in proportion to the increase in the number of sensory end organs and their nerve cells. Similarly the motor areas develop in importance in proportion to the development of the sensory centers. In addition, the motor elements in the brain, which in the lower forms are not distinctly related to the sensory elements, become more closely connected with them through numerous association fibers.

Significance of the Cerebral Cortex for Adaptive Behavior

The cerebral cortex is highly significant for it correlates the sensory impulses from the receptors or sense organs with the appropriate motor impulses to the effectors. The cerebrum of the lower vertebrates functions in this way, but does not allow for the variability in response possible in

man where an extraordinary number of association cells and fibers has been developed. That
this correlative activity between receptors and effectors is highly significant in the intelligent
adaptation of an individual to his environment is
illustrated in cases where there is a disturbance of
some special sense organ. In congenital deafness
or blindness development is definitely retarded,
and the defect in the important sense organ involved must be compensated for before the individual is able to compete on equal terms with
others. This is clearly shown in certain of the
lower vertebrates where, for example, when the
eyes are extirpated the animal behaves very much
as it does when the cerebral cortex is removed.
The disturbance of adaptive activity as a result of
cortical disturbance is most highly exemplified in
man and becomes of progressively less consequence with the descent in the evolutionary scale.
Extirpation of a given sensory center may have
little bearing on the future behavior of an animal
since the animal may not be dependent upon that
particular sensory mechanism, but extirpation of
a similar area of the human cortex may pro-
foundly influence the future behavior of the individual.

Chapter II

THE FUNCTIONAL SIGNIFICANCE OF THE HUMAN NERVOUS SYSTEM

THE WORKINGS OF THE NERVE CELL AND SYNAPSE

THE great range of sensibility and the flexibility of response in the human being are made possible only by a large number of nervous elements. The unit of the nervous system is the *neuron,* whose function is to conduct impulses. The neuron consists of a cell and its fibrous processes, the *dendrites* and the *axon.* The dendrites, or sensory processes, conduct impulses toward the cell body, and the axon, or motor process, conducts impulses away from it.

The neurons interact by the passage of impulses from the axon of one cell to the dendrites of another. The point at which an impulse passes from one nerve fiber to another is the synapse, which as we have seen presents an extremely small space, a structural gap. The *synaptic junction* is of great importance in human behavior for the following reasons:

Impulses are conducted in one direction only across the synapse. A nerve, either sensory or motor, can conduct an impulse in either direction, but the path of an impulse across a synapse is irreversible.

The reaction time of any sensori-motor response—that is, the time elapsing between stimulation of a sense organ and the resulting response—is influenced by the resistance which the impulse meets at the synapse. The number of synapses in a pathway is an important factor in the speed of a response, as we shall see in discussing the latent time of reflexes.

With repetition, the resistance at the synapse is lowered for a given type of impulse. "Pathways" are thus established in the nervous system, the impulses from certain sense organs giving rise to definite responses or habituated ways of reacting.

The nature of a response is influenced by any change in the conductibility of impulses across a synapse, such as may occur, for instance, following fatigue or the administration of certain drugs. After the use of strychnine, the resistance at the synapse is decreased, allowing an impulse to spread quickly in all directions. The widespread muscular activity that follows stimulation of a single sense organ, after strychnine is administered, illustrates the innumerable possibilities of response in the nervous system.

The adequacy of a stimulus is determined partially by the resistance the aroused impulses meet at the synapse. Many impulses initiated in a sense organ do not succeed in passing the synapse because they are unable to overcome the resistance at this junction. However, such ineffective stimuli, if repeated, may, as we shall see later, be summated, that is, they may acquire a cumulative effect and may not only succeed in passing one synapse but may overflow into other pathways. Such an irradiation of impulses explains the chaotic physical behavior of the young infant, for no definite pathways have as yet been established for his response to a stimulus.

The synaptic junctions are so arranged that an impulse passing along one sensory nerve may be transferred to many motor fibers. This structural arrangement is of great significance in making possible a wide variability of response. On the other hand, impulses from a number of receptors may converge into a common motor path thus allowing for a single coördinated response to various stimuli.

In the central nervous system the various fibers form bundles, or tracts, which pass up, by means of two or more neurons, to the cortex, or outer layer of the brain. No sensory impulse reaches the brain by means of one neuron only; one or more synapses are always found in the pathway leading to the cortical areas. The existence of

these synapses in the ascending pathways to the brain is significant in the explanation of "levels" of response. It makes possible a type of response which is not greatly dominated by the cortex. A stimulating condition may, therefore, result in a purely automatic reaction in which the brain plays only a minor rôle. This has given rise to various doctrines regarding the existence of "levels" in the nervous system, notably those of the English neurologist, Hughlings Jackson, who theorized about the existence of various "levels" of human behavior. A reaction which is reflex and automatic, controlled by the spinal cord, is less plastic than one which is controlled by centers in the brain below the cortex. Again, a response dominated by these centers is somewhat less modifiable than one dominated by the cortical centers of the brain.

Experimentation with animals shows the possibility of the existence of various levels of reactivity. When the spinal cord is cut across, impulses originating below the level of the cut cannot ascend to the brain, the responses possible are purely reflex in type, and similar to the reactions of lower animals which do not possess a brain. When the spinal cord and brain are intact with the exception of the cerebral cortex, the responses are less stereotyped and inflexible than when only the spinal cord functions. The decorticated animal shows little initiative, but is able to modify its responses somewhat, though its reaction possibilities are limited. When both the brain and spinal cord function normally, the responses brought about by impulses reaching the cortex are characteristically complex and variable, and of a wide range. The sense organs are closely integrated, and the responses resulting from various forms of stimulation can be correlated to give rise to a unified highly adaptive form of behavior.

The downward paths of the fibers from the brain also contain one or more synapses before reaching the muscles or glands which they activate, making it possible for an impulse to be transferred to motor fibers at various levels. This also allows for variabliity of responses ranging in character from the unguided reflex to controlled complex reactions.

THE SIGNIFICANCE OF THE RECEPTORS IN BEHAVIOR

The number and range of the receptor or sensory end organs are small in the lower animals, but they become increasingly greater in the scale of phylogenetic development, and they are to a great extent responsible for the development of intelligent behavior. Intelligent behavior is highly adaptive, and, together with control of the environment, depends to a large extent upon a highly developed receptor system enabling the organism to receive as much information as possible concerning the external world. Not only must the organism be receptive to varied types of stimuli, but the distance range of its receptivity must be wide. The unicellular organisms and other lower animals are able to receive stimuli only within a short distance from their bodies. This necessarily results in a narrow range of activity and allows the animal to adjust to the immediate environment only. With the development of receptors which are stimulated by conditions in a wide spatial range, the organism assumes activities of a more varied nature, and the adaptive responses, instead of being stereotyped, inflexible, and on a purely reflex level, become more variable, discriminative and intelligently adaptive.

We see how important the integrity of the receptors and of their connection with the central nervous system is to the behavior of the individual when we observe the reactions of people suffering from sensory defects. The disease known as *tabes dorsalis* (locomotor ataxia) in which the muscle, joint, and tendon sense is destroyed, gives a good example of defective adaptability. Manipulative habits of long standing are lost and walking, an almost purely reflex activity, is interfered with early in the course of the disease by unsteadiness and lack of motor control. Although muscular activity is not directly interfered with by the disease, habits and reflexes are lost because the impulses from the muscles and joints necessary to bring them about do not reach the central nervous system. The function of the receptors of the deep tissues is thus interfered with and the adaptive responses of the individual are disturbed. Interference with receptors which respond to objects at a distance, such as the eye or ear, creates an even more profound disturbance in the activities of the individual.

Functional Divisions of the Receptor Systems

The receptors have been classified by Sherrington, the English physiologist, according to their function, into the following groups:

(1) The *exteroceptors,* which receive stimuli from objects outside the body and initiate adjustments of the body as a whole. These include the end organs for vision, hearing, smell (also interoceptive), pain, temperature, pressure, and touch. Of these, the end organs for vision, hearing and smell are sometimes classified as distance receptors, and the end organs of the skin as direct receptors.

(2) The *interoceptors,* which have to do with internal adjustments of the body. These include

the sense organs for smell and taste, and the receptors concerned with nutritive and excretory processes, such as hunger, thirst, and distention of rectum and bladder.

(3) The *proprioceptors,* end organs located in the muscles, joints and tendons, are important in initiating impulses by which the individual becomes aware of the degree of muscular contraction, joint movements, or stretching of tendons, essential for the control of equilibrium and body movements.

The function of any receptor is to increase excitability toward one type of stimulus and to decrease it toward all others. The human ear, for example, is primarily sensitive only to air waves, the eye to light waves. However, there are some exceptions to this rule, notably the receptors for pain. Although these are usually stimulated by noxious stimuli, such as pinching, sharp instruments, and so on, extremes of heat or cold may also initiate impulses in pain nerves. The apparent specificity of the receptors has given rise to considerable controversy regarding the doctrine of *specific energies.* This doctrine states that a nerve when stimulated always gives rise to a particular type of sensation. It has been variously argued that the specificity of each sensory process is a function of (1) the end organ; (2) the particular nerve fibers and their tracts; or (3) the center in the brain where the nerves involved end. It is now generally admitted that sensory data are a function of the peripheral end organ, which responds specifically to particular types of stimuli, leading to specific types of reaction.

The Significance of the Distribution of the Receptors for Adaptive Reactions

The structure of the end organs for all of the sensory processes has not yet been satisfactorily identified by the anatomists. In the *exteroceptive* group there are, generally speaking, in addition to the distance receptors, the free nerve endings for pain, such as are found in the skin, similar free endings around the roots of hairs for touch, and special end organs of several varieties for pressure, touch and temperature.

The distribution of the end organs in the viscera and skin varies with the particular end organs and region of the body. The end organs for pressure are widely distributed in the viscera, but sensibility to touch and temperature is only slightly developed in the internal organs. The *peritoneum,* a membrane lining the abdominal and thoracic cavities (*parietal peritoneum*) and covering most of the internal organs (*visceral peritoneum*), is sensitive to pain only in its parietal parts. In the skin the end organs for touch, pain, and temperature are numerous and widely distributed. The number of these end organs in any part of the body is roughly proportional to the importance of that part in the adjustment activities of the individual. For example, the mucous membrane lining the mouth is less sensitive to temperature changes than the skin. The finger tips are much more sensitive to touch than the back of the hand or the posterior part of the body. The large number of manipulatory and other complex motor habits which man possesses are dependent upon this extreme sensitivity of the finger tips.

The distance exteroceptors, the eye and the ear, greatly extend the range of responses of which the animal is capable. These sense organs, more than any of the others, have increased the dominance of the organism over its environment by enabling it to obtain information concerning distant objects, thus increasing greatly its adaptive possibilities. It is generally stated that the eye is even more important than the ear since it is possible to localize stimuli far better with the aid of vision than with that of hearing. The binocular vision which man possesses is an additional factor in his ability to localize stimulating conditions accurately. Many advances in scientific work have been made mainly by means of the eye, following the development of aids to vision. Knowledge of astronomy, for example, has been furthered by the discovery of the telescope, and progress in medical science has been immeasurably helped by the use of the microscope. Many other examples could be cited of the importance of vision as a factor in the development of knowledge and the ability of man to react to an increasingly greater number of situations. The ear has also shared greatly in human development but its importance is perhaps less than that of vision in this regard.

Of the *interoceptors,* which have to do with the internal adjustments of the body, little is known concerning those found in the viscera, peritoneum, and mucous surfaces. The discomfort and pain from digestive disorders are due to stimulation of free nerve endings in the muscular coat of the intestinal canal as a result of the stretching and tension due to vigorous contraction of the intestines, and not to the direct stimulation by any noxious or toxic material in the alimentary tract. Muscular responses are probably also responsible for other types of visceral sensibility. Distention of the bladder, for example, initiates sensory impulses in its muscle wall, and the loss of these impulses produces a disturbance of normal physiological function.

The sensory quality of hunger is due to the rhythmical contraction of the stomach wall, and the intensity of this sensory process varies with the intensity and rapidity of the muscular contractions. No specific end organ for hunger is known, but it is possible that pain endings are stimulated as a result of the contraction waves which traverse the empty stomach. Pain occurs in long-continued hunger and corresponds with the strength and rapidity of the contractions of the stomach wall which increase as fasting is continued. This explains also the increased intensity of the responses of infants with the lapse of time following the missing of a feeding.

The *proprioceptors,* or sensory end organs of the skeletal muscles, joints, and tendons, are widely distributed. As we have seen, they furnish the individual with data regarding the position of various parts of his body and the state of contraction of his muscles, and by the continuous impulses originating in them, aid him to maintain equilibrium. They also aid in the development of fine coördinations and the performance of habits of manipulation involving complex groups of muscles. When the function of the proprioceptors is interfered with, the ability to make coördinated movements is partially lost. The ordinary activities of locomotion, such as walking and running, which involve a sequence of coördinated movements, are also dependent upon the functioning of these end organs. When the normal function is disturbed the individual may be unable to walk steadily, or even to maintain balance without the aid of vision. The actual muscular movements are not interfered with, except for a decrease in the tone of the muscles, indicating that the loss is sensory and not motor.

The proprioceptors, like the other sensory end organs, become increasingly sensitive with the repetition of their activities. They begin to function fairly efficiently early in the development of the human infant, as is evident from the rather fine coördinations which develop shortly after birth. Infants only a day or two old show well coördinated movements of the eyeballs in following a light, and at twelve days of age show good coördination of the arms in performing various movements. It is possible that a slow development of these muscular coördinations, sometimes seen in infants, may be due to a defective function of the proprioceptors.

THE MOTOR SYSTEM

Although a description of the development of motor activity in man involves a simultaneous account of the sensory nervous system, motor activity does occur in some of the lower animals, without corresponding specific sensory nervous elements. In organisms like the amoeba, the protoplasm probably acts as a sensory conductor of impulses. In the sponges, which have no sense organs, rings of contractile cells surrounding the pores are activated by direct stimulation of the water in which they live. Tracy,[1] of the University of Kansas, has shown that irregular movements are made by the embryos of certain species of toad fish, and the newly hatched larvae make definite movements before the sensory system is sufficiently developed to activate the motor mechanisms. It is suggested that these movements of the embryo have something to do with its escape from the egg membranes. Although muscular movements may take place without the presence of definite sensory cells, G. H. Parker,[2] the well-known zoölogist, has indicated that these cells develop as a means of bringing muscular tissue into action more quickly than by direct stimulation.

In all animals with a centralized nervous system and in man, the cell bodies of the neurons which bring about movements of the skeletal musculature are located entirely within the nervous system, whereas those for the sense organs are located in ganglia outside the brain and spinal cord. The fibers from the motor projection areas in the cerebral cortex end in the spinal cord, and there form a synapse with the second neuron, whose fibers are distributed to the body musculature. The

[1] Tracy, H. C. The development of motility and behavior reactions in the toad fish. Journal of comparative neurology, 1926, 40, 253–371.

[2] Parker, G. H. The elementary nervous system. Lippincott, Philadelphia, 1919, p. 114.

neurons above this synaptic junction are called the *upper motor* neurons, and those which send their fibers out directly to the muscles from the center in the spinal cord are called the *lower motor* neurons.

The extent to which the cerebral cortex controls bodily movements becomes evident when the function of the upper motor neurons is destroyed. When the *pyramidal tract,* the large motor path from the cerebral cortex, is interfered with by disease, the only responses possible are of a purely reflex type, initiated through the lower motor neurons, and are prolonged and exaggerated in extent. The cerebral cortex not only initiates muscular reactions but also controls their extent. In upper motor neuron lesions the amount of contraction of the muscles is also definitely increased and a spasticity, that is, a rigidity, results. Normally the skeletal muscles are in a state of partial contraction as a result of their continuous innervation by sensory impulses arising within the muscles themselves, and returning to them along the motor path of the reflex arc. When the regulatory control of the cortex is removed, the tension of the muscles is increased, leading to a condition of spasticity.

Interference with the lower motor neurons destroys the integrity of the reflex arc, and outgoing impulses along the motor nerves are abolished.

This results in a loss of muscular tone and a soft relaxed condition of the muscles supplied by the injured nerves.

THE REFLEX ARC

A reflex arc includes the receptor, the afferent conductor, which conveys the impulse to the nervous system, the central connecting (or association) neurons, the efferent conductor, which transmits the impulse to the motor end organs, and the effector, which may be either a muscle or gland. Even the simplest reflex thus involves a number of conduction paths in the central nervous system. Whether a reflex arc will be activated as a result of a given stimulating condition depends upon: (1) the quality, (2) the intensity, that is, strength, and (3) the duration of the stimulus. A significant function of the receptor is to lower its threshold of sensitivity for a certain kind or quality of stimulus—that is, to become more responsive to that type of stimulus—and to raise it (that is, become less responsive) for all other stimuli. The pupillary reflex is obtained by stimulating the eye with light, and is not obtained by any other stimulation. An infant ten days of age will respond to stimulation with water at 40° Centigrade, but not to water with a temperature of 25°. Similarly in adults, a pain stimulus which ordinarily does not elicit a response will do so when it is increased in intensity or in duration. Most of the reflexes easily illustrate this quantitative effect of the stimulus. In demonstrating the knee-jerk, for example, the stimulus (pressure) must be applied with a certain intensity or no response follows. The relationship between quantity of stimulation and intensity of response is such that within the limitations of the reactibility of the muscles (or glands), the greater the stimulating condition the more intense is the reaction.

Latent Time of Reflexes

One of the characteristics of reflex reaction is the phenomenon of *latent time*—the time elapsing between the application of the stimulus and the resulting response. The latent time of a reflex is in all cases much greater than the time necessary for an impulse to travel along the nerve tracts. When a motor nerve is stimulated directly, the latent time of response is exceedingly small compared to that of a reflex response which involves stimulation of the sense organ, transmission of impulses over the sensory and motor nerves, and activation of the motor end organ. Latent time, then, must be accounted for by retardation in the receptor, the synaptic junctions, or the effector, or in all three. It varies markedly with the type of reflex reaction exhibited, as is noted clearly in the sensori-motor responses of infants, the latent time of the response to touch being, for example, shorter than that of the response to pain.

One of the peculiarities of the latent time period is that it may be longer for stimuli which are biologically very important than for those which are relatively unimportant. For example, the response to pain is no doubt of greater importance for self-preservation than the response to touch, and yet the latent time of the latter is shorter. Sherrington has concluded that differences in the latent time of various responses are probably due to differences in the connecting pathways in the central nervous system. Although one cannot be positive of this conclusion, some evidence in its favor may be derived from an analysis of the difference in the pathways of the tracts for touch and for pain. There are probably but two synaptic junctions in the tracts for touch before they reach the brain, but the tracts for pain have many more synaptic junctions, being generally supposed to ascend in the spinal cord by "steps." There are, therefore, at least two factors in the central nervous system accounting for the difference in the latent time in any two reflex responses: (1) the number of synapses involved, and (2) the length of the conducting pathways. Obviously the length of the conducting fibers could not account for so marked a difference between the latent times of pain and touch when the same part of the body is stimulated and we must conclude that the synaptic junctions are responsible for most of the latent time. Some time, of course, is also consumed in the stimulation of the receptor and in the response of the effector after the impulse has reached it, but this accounts for only a fraction of the latent period.

Inhibition

Inhibition, the checking or suppression of a response, must be considered not as an absence of excitation, but as an activity similar to other responses to stimulation, as a process not different in kind from the stimulus-response process. The phenomenon of inhibition occurs in every activity, concomitantly with excitation. Since any muscular movement may occur in opposite directions, it is evident that a movement of a muscle in one direction must be accompanied by a relaxation of the opposing muscle. This is termed *reciprocal inhibition,* and has been shown by Sherrington to exist during all muscular responses. It is, indeed, essential to any type of coördinated activity. Inhibition of opposing musculature is seen in all gradations of reactions from the simple reflex response to the most complex coördinations of large groups of muscles. Its mechanism consists in the active innervation of the muscles opposing the overt bodily response, but in such a manner as to reduce them to a flaccid state of negative activity which allows the positively active muscles to respond in an adaptive fashion.

Inhibition of active responses may also occur. When a response is initiated by a stimulus of a certain intensity a sudden increase in that intensity often results in total inhibition of the response. Although the effect of a stimulating condition increases proportionately with its intensity, a point is finally reached where the stimulus, instead of causing a response, actually produces total inhibition. Again, a stimulus may interfere with a reaction when that stimulus is given during a response to another type of stimulation. The interference may be slight or it may take the form of a total inhibition, depending upon the strength of the inhibitory stimulus and its relation to the excitatory one. Stimulating circumstances which interfere with the completion of an activity probably act by blocking the original path, either somewhere in its peripheral course, or in the centers where the motor neurons are stopped from discharging impulses.

The cortex acts as a continual inhibitory mechanism in controlling the extent of the reflex responses. When cortical control is absent the reflex reactions are exaggerated and spasticity of the muscles results. The inhibitory function of the cortex is strikingly illustrated in neurological defects. In cases of post-encephalitis (after-effect of sleeping sickness) both in children and adults, all the physical and mental disturbances are the result of a lesion in the nervous system which disturbs many fibers whose functions are those of inhibition and control. These individuals develop spasticity of the muscles of the face and body resulting in motor difficulties. Their conduct disorders are manifested mostly as explosive emotional reactions and anti-social behavior. All of these disturbances are due to the inability of the individual to control his behavior in general.

Summation

Summation is a term applied to the cumulative effect of successively repeated stimuli. A stimulus which singly has not sufficient intensity to bring about a response, but which when repeated successively results in a reaction is called a *subliminal* stimulus. When a stimulus must be repeated in order to produce an effect, the successive applications must be given at what is found to be the most favorable interval; if too long a time elapses between the separate stimulations, the summation effect is lost regardless of the number given.

Summation is an important factor in many of the responses of infants and children, not only in sensory-motor reactions but also in other complex types of behavior. It is often necessary to repeat a stimulus frequently to a young child, because the threshold of sensitivity is high. It may be necessary to repeat a direction or a request quickly five or six times before a reaction follows. For such summation, there must also be a most favorable interval. In the application of complex stimuli such as those utilized in the training of infant and child, summation effects cannot be expected to occur unless the total interval during which the repetitions are made is relatively short. Parents often complain that a child does not react quickly even to two or three identical requests. In such cases it is important that the direction be repeated in a relatively short time. The repetition of a direction allows the child to grasp its meaning, and produces a summation effect similar to that noted in the summation of simpler subliminal stimuli. It is often possible to so lower the threshold of reactivity in infants and children by quickly repeated stimulation that after a period of such training the number of stimulations necessary for a response is markedly smaller. From the standpoint of training, therefore, the importance of repetition must be emphasized.

Chapter III

THE FIRST HUMAN RESPONSES

THE APPEARANCE OF SENSORI-MOTOR RESPONSES. THEIR NATURE AND ADAPTIVE FUNCTION

THE first overt bodily reactions of the newborn infant are simple sensori-motor responses which are strikingly undefined, uncoördinated and aimless. With the increase in age and experience these reactions of the bodily musculature become guided and usefully coördinated, indicating that most of the complex behavior of the growing infant is the result of a direct learning activity rather than the manifestation of inherited modes of response. Out of the vague, undifferentiated behavior of the infant are built up the characteristically adaptive responses seen later in life. At birth the learning process has already begun, and rapid improvement is made in the first hours of life.

The simplest reactions shown by the newborn infant are the reflex responses. Just as the accuracy and adaptiveness of gross bodily movements improve with experience, so some of the reflexes can also be shown to improve in adequacy after birth; in fact, it is highly probable that before birth all the reflexes begin to develop in a manner not unlike the learning process.

The presence and completeness of any of the first reflexes depend upon the adequacy of the five components of the reflex arc, namely, the receptor, the afferent conducting path, the central connections, the efferent conducting path, and the effector. Each of these components must be capable of reacting to a stimulating condition in order that an overt response may take place. It is sometimes stated that the adequacy of a stimulus is determined by its ability to initiate an impulse in the receptor. Experimental evidence has shown, however, that many impulses actually initiated in the receptor do not result in an overt activity because of the ineffectiveness of other components of the reflex arc.

A reflex is sometimes defined as an invariable response to a constant stimulus; that is, when the stimulating condition is the same the resulting response is said to be always of the same type, both qualitatively and quantitatively. Variations in the reflex responses of the newborn infant are such, however, that this definition must be qualified in two ways. In the first place, not all so-called simple stimuli are equally adequate in producing a response. This is illustrated by the fact that a slight tactual stimulus applied to the infant is followed by a response, whereas a pain stimulus of greater intensity does not result in an overt reaction. For example, in an infant below twelve to eighteen hours of age, a slight touching or tickling of the nasal mucous membrane will produce sneezing, or a mild stroking of the sole of the foot will bring about withdrawal of the leg, but a needle prick on the foot fails to produce an overt reaction.

In the second place, we must question the interpretation of the term "invariability" as applied to the responses of the growing infant. If an "invariable response" is one that does not change, then the reflexes of an infant are not invariable. A newborn infant does not respond when the sole of its foot is pricked with a needle, but after the infant has reached the age of about 18 hours, this stimulus is followed by withdrawal of the leg. In other words, the reflex response to a pain stimulus applied to certain parts of the body is not present at birth, but appears after a certain number of hours. Furthermore, within certain age limits the reflex responses to certain constant stimuli change in that they improve. This is illustrated by the reaction of the pupil to light, a response which in many infants is not present at birth, but appears within a few hours and rapidly increases in amount and speed until the reflex is perfected. These changes are probably due to the experiential development of the end organs and of the central nerve connections.

Although some of the reflexes are present in a workable fashion at birth, such as swallowing, closing the eyes upon stimulation of the cornea, and response to deep pressure, others have not appeared or are only in a rudimentary state. Sucking is present in all infants after 24 hours, but before that time is frequently difficult to elicit. Nurses in hospital nurseries report that many infants can not suck a rubber finger put into the mouth and have to be taught to feed. In these cases sucking is often started by putting a few drops of milk or sweetened water into the mouth. From this time on the adequacy of the response improves steadily and rapidly. Similarly, other reflexes can be shown to develop with the repetition of the act, at a rate which differs for the different reflexes. The discrepancy in the rate of development may be due in part to the fact that all parts of the body of the newborn infant are not equally sensitive but vary markedly in this respect during the early hours of life when the infant is first subjected to the stimulating conditions of the external environment.

The first reflex responses to appear are those which are of particular value in defensive adjustments. Sucking and swallowing are necessary for feeding and survival. Sneezing, already mentioned as one of the first reflex reactions, is purely a defensive activity, since it brings about a rapid expulsion of air from the nostrils and thus tends to remove a noxious stimulus. The mucous membranes are most sensitive to contact and mild irritation, and they are also most easily injured by noxious stimuli. In general, there seems to be a direct relationship between the reactivity of a structure and its liability to injury. A possible exception may be seen in the case of the response to a pain stimulus which is not so rapid as to touch. The probable conditioning of the infant during its intrauterine life may be a factor in altering this relationship.

Little is known about the activity of the infant or of the stimuli which it receives during its intrauterine life. The existence of the foetus in a fluid medium, however, introduces several conditioning factors which exert an influence upon the infant's first responses. The surrounding amniotic fluid protects the foetus from sharp stimuli and by its buffer effect reduces the intensity of any sudden massive stimulus. Temperature and touch are two types of stimuli which are probably constantly present. The temperature of the amniotic fluid, however, since it is constant, and since a stimulating condition at any given point can produce a response only when it differs sufficiently in quality or in intensity from the condition just preceding it, cannot properly be called a stimulating condition. It exerts very little influence upon any conditioning process of the foetus. But the sudden change in temperature at birth contributes to the explosive reaction noted in almost every newborn.

Because of the movements of the mother and of the foetus itself, tactile stimulation occurs frequently, if not almost constantly, in intrauterine life. Up to the seventh or eighth month the foetus is constantly changing positions; at times it is protected on all sides by the amniotic fluid, and at other times it lies very close to the wall of the uterus. This means not only that it receives tactile stimuli frequently but also that the type of contact changes. Now we have seen that as the number of impulses which pass over a nerve tract is increased, the threshold of irritability of the receptor and the interspersed synapses is decreased, and that the number of stimuli received is thus one of the factors determining the sensitivity of any receptor. The lowering in the foetus during intrauterine life of the threshold of excitability to touch, therefore, in part determines the sensitivity of the newborn infant to that type of stimulus. Minkowski, a Swiss neurologist, in observing the behavior of two to five month foetuses removed by caesarean operation, was able to elicit reflex movements of the head, trunk and extremities at two months, by a slight touch on the skin. These movements, which were diffuse, uncoördinated and non-specific, tending to irradiate over the entire body, illustrate the early appearance of responsiveness to tactual stimulation.

Reflex responses to deep pressure are also present for the most part at birth, but the manifestation of some of them differs from that in older children and adults. The knee jerk and the biceps and triceps reflexes can be demonstrated, although this is sometimes difficult. The plantar reflex may be elicited very easily by light pressure on the sole of the foot. The typical response to this stimulus in the child or adult is a flexion of the toes, especially the great toe, but in about fifty percent of cases the infant extends its great toe.

At birth stimulation of the visceral sensory apparatus also results in a prompt response. Stimulation of the larynx or pharynx induces an immediate cough. Swallowing and the excretory processes are all adequate.

The newborn infant is thus able to respond to many stimuli, but his gross bodily reactions are nevertheless unadaptive and not well coördinated. Structurally the motor elements of the reflex are develop before the corresponding sensory elements. The first intrauterine activity of the foetus is thus probably entirely motor, that is, movements are initiated and continued without any definite corresponding sensory elements. It may be that these reactions are initiated by the metabolic activity of the muscles themselves. Such activity must be aimless and uncoördinated in type since there is no stimulus present toward which the response may be directed. When the sensory elements appear, muscular activity can become more definitely coördinated. However, muscular coördination is developed only to a small degree at birth, but the conditioning of the infant during its first few days of life rapidly increases its coördinated activity. We know that the first activity of the newborn infant is characterized by its uncoördinated and undifferentiated reactions. The cry, the movements of the arms and legs, and the general bodily activity are due in part to the new stimulating conditions encountered during the birth process. Some of the automatic physiological functions are also partly initiated by these changed stimulating conditions which result from the new environment. Breathing, for example, is started by the accumulation of carbon dioxide due to the loss of the uterine circulation, and is helped by external stimuli such as change in temperature and mechanical excitation in handling.

THE DEVELOPMENT OF RESPONSES IN VARIOUS PARTS OF THE BODY

The development of responses varies considerably in different parts of the body. Responses to pain appear earlier in the anterior (upper) end of the body, and develop more rapidly than those in the posterior (lower) parts. This is due to the fact that the upper end possesses greater sensitivity.

This variation is illustrated by the different amounts of stimulation which must be applied to the different regions of the infant's body to produce a response. The face of the newborn infant is sooner and more sensitive to a painful stimulus than the legs, and this continues so up to about the fourth day of life. Figure 5 shows the average number of needle pricks necessary to produce a response when applied to the legs and to the face. The response to this stimulus consists of a pulling away of the legs or face, with movements of the arms and crying. The average number of stimuli necessary to produce a response is at all ages smaller for the face than for the legs. Sometimes infants less than six hours of age do not respond at all to as many as ten needle pricks on the legs. After five days every normal infant responds to a single needle prick on the face, but until about the

seventh day there is no response to a similar painful stimulus applied to the legs.

There are at least two factors determining the
comparatively greater sensitivity of the anterior
end of the body. First, the nerves for touch and
pain have fewer synapses in the face and head re-

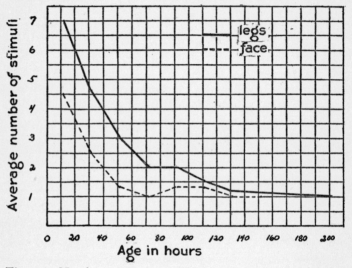

Fig. 5. Number of pain stimuli necessary to produce a
response.

gions than in the extremities. The threshold at
the synapses is higher in the newborn infant than in
the adult, as many impulses have not yet passed
over the nerve tracts, and impulses which must
pass over a great many synapses have less chance
to complete the final path. Secondly, the distance
which an impulse has to traverse is greater for the

posterior end of the body than for the face and head.

A biological explanation may also be given. Physiologists have shown that in many organisms *metabolic activity,* or the process of chemical change in living cells, is greater in the anterior than the posterior end of the body. Increased irritability and rate of conduction of impulses accompany this increased metabolic rate. We have seen how, in the evolution from simpler to more complex animal forms, the anterior end began very early to assume dominance over the rest of the body. This was accomplished mainly by the development of a central nervous system, although some physiological differentiation occurred even where the nervous system was only roughly localized. With the development of a definite central nervous system, and especially of a brain, the metabolic activity and physiological significance of the anterior end lead to its definite domination.

THE DEVELOPMENT OF REFLEX AND SENSORI-MOTOR ACTIVITY

The behavior of the newborn infant in response to specific sensory stimuli is strikingly aimless and inadequate. Only gradually with the lowering of the threshold of excitability do his responses become certain and typical. Early theories of human instinct were no doubt based upon the assumption that newborn infants are able to respond in a fairly uniform manner to many types of stimulation and that other mechanisms appear later, ready to function when the organism attains a sufficient degree of maturity. The sex instinct, for example, was said to appear at puberty, and the fact was ignored that at this time marked physiological changes occur which make it possible for an adolescent to respond to so-called sexually exciting stimuli. The theory of an instinct of self-preservation implies that the newborn infant is inherently able to adapt himself to noxious stimuli. The reflex mechanisms, however, are not inherently capable of functioning regardless of the environment. Tracy [1] has shown that "the newly hatched toad fish larva does not react to any stimulus which would be presented to it in its normal environment." It does not respond to tactile stimulation anywhere on the outside skin, and its first tactile reactions appear from stimulation on the mucous membrane of the floor of the mouth. These reactions undergo a gradual development from uncertain, atypical responses to perfected reactions. Embryos such as these developing in a non-fluid medium are not subjected to the stimuli offered by the amniotic fluid in higher animals where the environment is such that the end organs begin to

[1] Op. cit.

receive stimuli early in the process of development.

In man the nervous system has reached such a degree of plasticity and variability that most of the responses which develop are dependent upon the type of influences to which the organism is subjected. These responses are inadequately developed at birth and increase in specificity with the acquisition of experience. It has been maintained that the development in adequacy of the reflexes does not preclude the existence of an inherent factor, and that responses mature rather than develop through experience only. The growth in the adequacy of both the reflex and sensori-motor reactions, however, is related so closely to the amount of stimulation the infant receives that the existence of a developmental process similar to that noted in any act of learning seems evident.

The response of the pupil to light is a reflex not ordinarily regarded as showing much variability under normal conditions, yet many observers have noted that there is a difference in the extent and rapidity of the pupillary contraction in infants of different ages. When this response is observed from birth it is found that its adequacy increases up to about thirty hours of age, after which the reaction is good in most cases. This rapid increase in the adequacy of the reaction exemplifies a greatly accelerated learning process during the first hours of the infant's exposure to changes in lighting conditions. Although early investigators in anatomy, like Flechsig, found that nervous function in general depends upon the structural development of nerve paths, no evidence has been produced to show that the actual reflex arc for the pupillary reaction is markedly different in a newborn infant and in an infant four or five days of age. Yet the response of the pupil to light is markedly inferior in a newborn infant to that in an older infant. Since the pupillary response does increase in adequacy, and no differences in the structure of the reflex arc appear, the change in the reaction must be a result of the growing experience of the infant.

Investigations by anatomists and physiologists show that the structural pathways for reflex responses are present and well developed at birth; indeed, that they are quite well developed long before the end of the gestation period. The improvement of reflex responses, then, must be explained in terms of function rather than in terms of structural development after birth. Growth in the adequacy of a response implies the fashioning of the pattern of the nerve tracts over which the requisite impulses pass. An outstanding. difference between the responses of an infant and those of a child or adult is the threshold of irritability. In the newborn infant, the resistance offered to many types of stimuli is very high; even during handling the infant will often fall asleep. This high threshold of irritability is probably caused by resistance, but it is difficult to state specifically whether along the whole nervous arc, in parts of the conducting mechanism, or at the synaptic junctions. Presumably conditioning of responses goes on by changes at the synapse, and possibly the development of adequate responses in infants depends upon similar changes in response at the synapse. The synaptic junctions of newborn infants are imperfectly developed mechanisms over which many impulses must travel before certain patterns are established. The function of the synapse, as we have seen, is to offer resistance, to send the impulse in one direction only, and to lower the threshold for one type of stimulus and heighten it for all others. Assuming, then, that the synapse in a newborn infant has not been fully conditioned, the threshold will be high at this junction, and repetition of stimuli is necessary before pathways can be established. What particular pathways are established will depend upon the general structural relationships between the afferent and efferent nerve tracts and upon the functional relationships arising as a result of individual experience.

Just as the pupillary reaction and the response to pain grow more adequate, other sensori-motor processes can be shown to improve in adaptiveness with the increase in experience of the infant. Although the response to touch is present at birth and may be elicited by stimulation almost anywhere over the surface of the body, its adequacy is developed only by repetition of the stimulus. A particular stimulus may produce a reaction but the adaptive quality of many reactions must be developed. It is quite possible that the same relation between experience and adequacy of response holds for all the true reflexes, and that those which are perfected at birth have become so as a result of the intrauterine experience of the infant. Adaptability is related to a lowering of the threshold along certain arcs and a heightening along others in the response to particular stimuli.

THE DEVELOPMENT OF COÖRDINATED ACTIVITY. THE FACTOR OF TRAINING

The development of coördinated activity in newborn infants illustrates clearly the rôle of experience and of the learning process in sensori-motor responses. Coördination of the eyes may be tested by moving a dim flashlight to and fro within a range of about fifteen inches in front of an infant's face, in a darkened room. A successful coördination is one in which the axes of the eyeballs do not deviate during the movement of fixating upon the light. When the number of successful coördinations of the two eyeballs is noted, and a ratio obtained of the number of imperfect movements to the total number of eye movements made during the test, a measure is available of the percentage of error made. For example, if the infant makes three uncoördinated movements of the eyeballs in a total of fifteen eye movements during the test period, the percent of error is $\frac{3}{15}$, or twenty percent. Observation of less than about fifteen eye movements does not give a fair test of a child's ability.

Figure 6 shows the percentage of error in the coördinated movements of the eyeballs in a group of normal infants. The average error was 52.2 percent for the youngest age group, and it decreased rapidly with the increase in age up to 50 hours. Above this age there was considerable fluctuation, but in general a decrease occurred with the increase in age. Above the age of 200 hours all infants tested showed good coördination, that is, their percentage of error was 0.0. In some very young infants the coördination of the eyeballs is good in one direction, but poor when the direction of rotation of the eyeballs is changed. For example, when the eyes are turned to the right, all the coördinations made may be good, but when turned to the left, imperfect coördinations or deviations occur. Dearborn,[1] who made observations of the

[1] Dearborn, G. V. N. Moto-sensory development. Warwick and York, Baltimore, 1910. Pp. 215.

first three years of a child, states that the eyes were
perfectly coördinated the first few minutes after
birth, but adds later that the infant showed a mo-

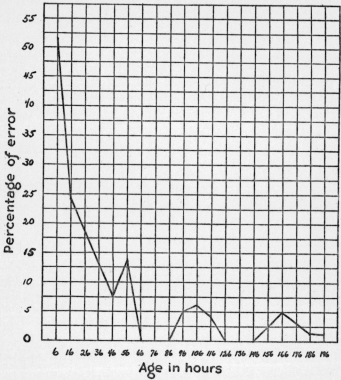

Fig. 6.   Coördination of the eyeballs in following a light.

mentary internal strabismus (turning in) of one
eye on the 12th day, and on the 52nd day "was
badly cross-eyed" at times.   Miss Shinn,[1] during

[1] Shinn, M. W.   Notes on the development of a child.   University
of California Publications, 1907, 4, p. 24.

her detailed study of one infant, observed no rudiment of coördination during the first two weeks of life. Mrs. Blanton,[1] working with Watson in the psychological laboratory of the Johns Hopkins Hospital, noted inequality of eye movements, and states that some babies have a "hint of cross eyes," one eye moving faster than the other. Gutman,[2] in a comprehensive study of the reaction of infants to a light stimulus, states that coördination of the eyeballs is seen in some newborn infants, but that the infant learns this coördination just as he learns to coördinate any other group of muscles. Jones,[3] in a recent study of the early behavior of infants, observed that true fixation of the eyes is not present at birth, and concluded that the period of development for eye coördination is between 33 and 90 days.

The lack of agreement among these experimenters is probably due to variations in technique and differences in objective. It is well known that newborn infants keep their eyes open only for a very brief time in a lighted room, and it is very difficult to observe the process of fixation unless

---

[1] Blanton, M. G. The behavior of the human infant during the first thirty days of life. Psychological review, 1917, 24, p. 461.

[2] Gutmann, M. I. Über Augenbewegungen der Neugeborenen und ihre theoretische Bedeutung. Archiv für die Gesamte Psychologie, 1924, 47, p. 108.

[3] Jones, M. C. The development of early behavior patterns in young children. Pedagogical seminary and Journal of genetic psychology, 1926, 33, 537–585.

the light stimulus is employed in a darkened room. Some experimenters have studied the process of coordination by giving the stimulus in a darkened room, others in a light room; some have observed the coördination of the eyeballs during random movements, others have studied the ability of infants to fixate and follow a light stimulus steadily. The normal newborn infant is undoubtedly able to fixate a white light, but the coördination of the eyeballs is not good in that a number of deviations or uncoördinated movements are usually made in a series of successive movements. With the increase in the age of the infant the amount of error decreases up to the age of about 200 hours, when good coördination is attained. However, momentary strabismus is sometimes noted in infants above this age, especially when the movements of the eyeballs are rapid.

Coördination of the arms and hands may be studied by eliciting defense reactions by continuous pressure with the forefinger on the infant's chin. The number of arm movements which the infant makes before a perfect coördination results is counted; a perfectly coördinated movement is one in which both of the infant's hands touch the distal end of the examiner's finger in a pushing motion with accuracy and precision.

Figure 7 shows the number of arm movements made before a perfect coördination results in infants of different ages. The majority of infants below 20 hours of age are unable to make a perfectly coördinated defensive movement of the two arms and hands. In infants from 20 to 40 hours of age an average of eleven arm movements is

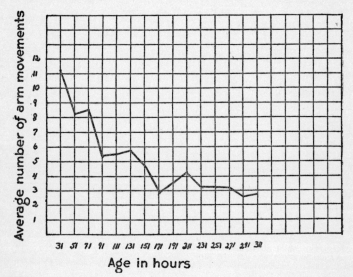

Fig. 7. Coördination of the arms in response to pressure on the chin.

necessary before such a coördinated movement is made. With the increase in age these defensive movements become less indefinite and irregular, and the number necessary for a perfect coördination decreases fairly regularly. Infants as old as 320 hours (somewhat over thirteen days), however, are still unable to make an immediate perfectly coördinated defense reaction of the two arms. It is a common observation that older children can make a perfectly coördinated response to such a stimulus in one trial only. As this defensive reaction of pushing away a noxious stimulus is poorly developed at birth, although the muscles are sufficiently strong to allow rapid and active movements, it is demonstrated that there is no pre-existing mechanism, perfected and ready to function, which allows the human infant "instinctively" to protect itself by definite, coördinated and adaptive movements of the arms and hands. Even the responses of self-preservation, which are generally accepted as instinctive, must be assumed to develop as actual reactions through experience.

The improvement of coördination of the arms is fairly rapid at first and then increases gradually with slight variation. A comparison of this curve of improvement with the typical learning curve of any habit shows a great similarity between the two in the continued increase in ability, the rapid initial improvement, and the later slow increase toward perfection. Analysis of the development of coördinated responses of a protective nature in newborn infants indicates a close similarity to the process of habit formation in the development of any motor act; in other words, they are habits of skill based upon practice.

Probably many human responses that are ordinarily termed instinctive will prove upon analysis to be products of the learning process. In the lower animals, the newborn is able to make many of the responses of the adult, and quickly develops all of its possible reactions. The higher the animal, the less able is it to adjust to the environment at birth. The period of human infancy is relatively so long and the helplessness of the infant so great that practically all of the behavior that develops is the result of training. The greater the number of fixed connections and instinctive modes of action an animal possesses, the less habit formation figures in its development. Intelligent behavior depends upon the ability to modify reactions, and develops, as we have seen, with the possession of an increasingly flexible nervous system.

The Influence of Age upon Coördinated Responses

A direct correlation exists between age and the development in adequacy of the sensori-motor responses. This fact is sometimes utilized to show that maturation of the organism (growth of neural arcs and end organs) is responsible for the improvement in sensori-motor activity. The factor of age, however, introduces the important condition of repeated stimulation; an infant ten days of age has received much more stimulation than an infant one day old, and has had an opportunity to learn by trial and error. From the beginning the infant makes trial and error responses to stimuli and the adequacy of his final responses is dependent upon the frequency of such activity. When stimulations are given close together the development of coördination is much more rapid than when they are given infrequently and casually, as the infant receives them in the ordinary environment. This indicates that many of the responses usually attributed to organic maturation are in reality products of learning, since such a speeding up of adaptive behavior could not take place were maturation necessary for its growth.

If a control group of infants could be kept under conditions excluding the normal stimuli of the nursery, as in an incubator, it is highly probable that the reactions of these infants would be much inferior to those of the average infant in his normal environment. This also would indicate clearly the significance of the learning process in the development of reflex and other sensori-motor responses, and the failure of maturation alone to bring about this development.

Breed and Shepard's experiments with the pecking response of chicks showed that when chicks were prevented from pecking for a time they were less accurate in seizing and swallowing grains when finally allowed to peck than chicks not restrained from pecking, but the adequacy of their response improved more rapidly. These writers concluded that the increase in adequacy came about in part through practice and in part as a result of maturation. However, the rate of improvement was in every respect similar to that shown in any learning curve, such as characterizes the formation of habits in adults, where maturation cannot be a factor.

When a chick is not allowed to peck, only one of the many responses necessary in this reaction is restrained. The animals were free to use their legs, wings and other musculature. In any learning process the final response comprises the reaction of a particular group of muscles only, but before such a group of muscles can react alone, many other muscular responses are brought into play. In pecking, the final response probably depends upon the equilibrium of the body and the control of the head, leg and neck muscles. The process of maturation is thus complicated by many learning activities, which must have been effective in the rapid improvement of the chicks that had been prevented from pecking.

Certain responses may be said to maturate only when the reaction is dependent upon structure which is at first not sufficiently developed for a given response. Locomotion, for example, depends upon the existence of a structure necessary to carry out this muscular act. Certain muscular and nervous structures must be present before the infant is able to maintain equilibrium. The muscles must be long enough and sufficiently strong to support the body. In this respect it may be said that maturation of structure is a phase of the habit of locomotion. Similarly in any manipulatory habit, the size of the hand and fingers and the strength and flexibility of the muscles must be sufficient to allow for perfect manipulations. However, even where structural development is essential, it alone does not account for the increase in the adequacy of a response. The ability to coördinate muscular activities is just as important as the size or strength of muscles, and such coordination develops as the result of a learning process. The structure of the organism matures, but sensori-motor activities are perfected through practice.

THE INFLUENCE OF THE HIGH THRESHOLD OF IRRITABILITY IN INFANTS UPON THEIR REFLEX ACTIVITY

As we have already seen, the function of the receptor is to lower the threshold, that is, increase the excitability towards one type of stimulation, and raise the threshold or decrease excitability to-

wards all others. Discriminatory responses are
thus made possible. If the threshold of each receptor were not lowered for one type of stimulation only, many different stimuli would elicit similar responses. In newborn infants the threshold
of irritability is high for all types of stimulation.
This is evident in the amount of time the young
infant spends in sleep; because the threshold is
high, he is unable to respond to many outside stimuli, and relaxation and sleep result. The infant
fails to respond, not because of structural differences in the receptors or the motor end organs, but
because the high threshold of excitability makes
ordinary stimuli ineffective in crossing the synapses. Many stimuli which ordinarily produce
responses in children do not do so in infants, showing that the threshold of irritability has become
lower with the increase in the number of stimuli
which have passed over the reflex arcs.

Not only does the newborn infant fail to respond to certain types of stimuli, but some of his
reactions are different in character from those of
the child or adult. An example of this difference
is the response to stimulation of the plantar surface of the foot. When stroking the sole of the
foot is followed by a flexion of the toes, especially
of the great toe, this is termed a "negative Babinski sign." When the response is an extension of
the toes it is called a "positive Babinski." As we

have seen, the typical response to this stimulation in
the adult is a flexion of the toes, but the infant extends its great toe in about fifty percent of cases.
However, additional stimulations will usually
cause this response of extension to change to a flexion. When the sole of the infant's foot is
repeatedly stimulated within one-half minute the
summation effect is such that a positive response is
changed to a negative, but when this interval is
markedly increased, the usual summation effect is
not observed.   An optimal or most favorable interval, therefore, exists within which the successive
stimulations must be given in order to be effective.
Under these conditions the final response in at
least ninety percent of infants is flexion. This
change from extension to flexion with continued
stimulation is not due to fatigue of the muscles
since continued stimulation in those cases showing
an initial flexion of the toes never results in an
extension; in fact, as the stimulus is continued in
these cases the contraction of the flexed muscles
increases in intensity.

Many investigators have concluded that the
presence of a positive Babinski in infants is the
result of structural defects in the nervous system.
Often it is attributed to the lack of complete ana-
tomical development of the pyramidal tract (the
large motor path from the cerebral cortex to the
spinal cord), with resulting failure of transmis-

THE FIRST HUMAN RESPONSES   89

sion of impulses along the nerve fibers involved.
This explanation does not account, however, for
the fact that the reaction is not consistently that
of an extension of the toes, and that it varies from
time to time in the same infant. A recent investigator, Feldman,[1] states as a result of his histo-
logical work upon the nerve tracts of infants, that
the pyramidal tract is sufficiently developed to allow free transmission of impulses. His explanation of the Babinski phenomenon is that the transmission of impulses along this tract is effected by
rapid blood changes which alternately block the
impulses or allow them to pass. Ordinary stimuli
which are sufficient to bring out a reaction in
adults are frequently inadequate in producing a
response in newborn infants, and this inadequacy
may be due to the blocking of impulses by the high
threshold of irritability of the infant's sense organs and synaptic junctions.

Kleitman's [2] observations of the Babinski reflex
in adults who had been kept awake for long periods and were sleeping following the period of insomnia, showed that the response was invariably
that of extension, while in the normal sleeping and
waking periods of these subjects the reflex was invariably negative. His explanation is that dur-

[1] Feldman, W. M. The nature of the plantar reflex in early life
and the causes of its variations. American journal of diseases of
children, 1922, 23, 1–40.
[2] Kleitman, N. Studies on the physiology of sleep. American
journal of physiology, 1923, 66, 67–92.

ing the period of sleep following insomnia the threshold is greatly raised and there is a functional block in the nerve tracts. He has also observed that continued application of the stimulus in the ordinary manner causes a change from the positive to the negative response, and concludes that this is due to the overcoming of synaptic resistance through the summation of subliminal (quantitatively inadequate) stimuli.

Since the positive Babinski sign may be due to a high threshold of irritability and a functional blocking of the nerve tracts, it is not to be considered necessarily as pathological. In the examination of the nervous system of young infants this factor must be taken into account before conclusions are reached concerning the presence of abnormalities.

Chapter IV

THE RELATION OF SENSORI-MOTOR DEVELOPMENT TO THE GROWTH OF INTELLIGENCE

THE FIRST SIGNS OF INTELLIGENCE

THE first signs of intelligence in the newborn infant are manifested in sensori-motor responses, and the development of intelligence is directly related to the development of these reactions. Phylogenetically, increase in intelligent behavior goes hand in hand with the increase in number, sensitivity and integration of sense organs and in coördination of various muscle groups into functional units. The varied behavior of any animal is limited by the number of sensory processes and the complexity of muscular arrangement which it possesses, and the advance of man has depended upon his equipment of sense organs and his capacity to develop varied motor activities and a wide range of manipulatory habits.

The ability of an individual to adjust to new situations depends upon his capacity to react to environmental stimuli and to retain information obtained through the sense organs for directing future behavior, and upon the possession of a flexible muscular system which permits complex combinations of motor activities. The arrangement of the muscles of the human arm and hand shows an advance over that of the animal and illustrates the relationship between muscular flexibility and the development of intelligence.

Examples of the increasing ability to adjust to environmental conditions may be found in many biological situations. In lower animals, such as the frog, the temperature of the body is adjusted to the environment. The warm blooded animals, however, acquire a regulatory physiological mechanism whereby a relatively constant body temperature is maintained, irrespective of environmental influences, and which thus gives them greater independence of temporary or even permanent changes in their environment. As we go higher in the phylogenetic scale we see a more complex type of adjustment to changes in the environment made possible by the increase in the range of activities of which the animal makes use. The monkey is distinctly superior to other animals, not so much because of structural differences as because it is able to utilize objects in its environment for better adaptation. Professor Yerkes, of Yale University, and the German psychologist, Köhler, have both shown that the chimpanzee and the young child are markedly similar in their ability to use tools in many of their reactions. This ability to alter environmental conditions develops because of two interdependent factors: the increasing range of the sensory apparatus and the increasing complexity and flexibility of the muscular arrangement. On the basis of this development, man is able not only to adjust to his environment, but to alter his environmental situation and to free himself from its limitations.

The newborn infant has at his command a complex system of receptors and effectors, but he has not at first the ability to correlate these two systems. If we define intelligence as the ability to adjust to new situations, the intelligence of the newborn infant is very slightly developed, but as with age and experience his gross bodily responses become guided and usefully coördinated, an increase in intelligence occurs. A coördinated response to a stimulus is effective and consequently more intelligent than the vague and uncoördinated responses the infant first shows. The increase in the range of stimuli to which he reacts and the increase in the complexity of his muscular responses are definite criteria of growth in intelligence, for they are directly correlated with the flexibility of his adjustment to his environment.

The relation of sensori-motor development to intelligence may also be noted in older children and even in adults. It was at one time popularly believed that so-called mechanical ability had no definite relation to intelligence and that actually an inverse relationship between mechanical ingenuity and "abstract" intelligence might exist. According to this conception an individual backward or defective in intelligence might be superior in mechanical ability. Recent experiments, however, have shown that individuals who have good intelligence according to the usual criteria do better in tests of mechanical ability than mentally defective individuals. There are, of course, exceptions to this general statement. Children and adults of superior intelligence are often uninterested in mechanical tasks and because of this lack of interest and the consequent lack of training, the direct relationship between intelligence and manipulatory ability may not be apparent.

Some evidence has lately been advanced to show the influence of environment and training upon the development of intelligence in children. The earliest manifestation of intelligence is seen in the sensori-motor responses, and intelligent growth can be followed by observing the degree of perfection of these reactions. Since they improve with practice, the growth of intelligence must be determined at least in part by the amount of stimulation and training offered by the environment. Doctor Paul Furfey of the Catholic University of America has recently found that the intelligence of infants less than one year of age has no relation to the social status and economic condition of their parents. Since such a relation has been shown to exist in the case of older children, it must be due to the more stimulating environment of better as compared with poorer homes. Freeman [1] showed that foster children placed in an improved environment make a significant gain in intelligence. Those placed in better homes gain considerably more than those in poorer homes. Also, those who are adopted at an early age gain more than those adopted at a later age, showing that an improved environment and better training are most effective in influencing intelligence during the early plastic period of the child's life.

Correlation between Sensori-motor Responses and other Estimates of the Development of Intelligence in the Infant

Existing measures of the intelligence of the infant and young child are based upon the range of sensitivity of the sense organs and the complexity of responses of which he is capable. In testing the infant or young child, certain physical accom-

[1] Freeman, F. N., Holzinger, K. J., and Mitchell, B. C. The influence of environment on the intelligence, school achievement and conduct of foster children. 27th Yearbook, National Society for the Study of Education, Pt. I, 1928, 107–217.

plishments are used, such as the ability to sit up, to stand and later to walk and to utter sounds, all of which are directly correlated with intellectual progress. The relation between time of first walking and talking and various criteria of intelligence is such that early walking and talking seem to indicate early mental development. In mentally defective children walking and talking almost invariably begin late compared with normal children. Mead [1] has shown by a statistical study that the median age at which walking begins in normal children is 13.54 months, and talking 15.80 months. The histories of schoolable feeble-minded children showed that they began to walk at a median age of 21.6 months and to talk at 34.4 months. According to these results normal children walk on the average 8 months earlier than feeble-minded children, and talk 18 months earlier. Children with a more severe grade of feeble-mindedness walk and talk even later than the schoolable types. In contrast with these results Terman [2] finds in his study of gifted children that they walk at a median age of 12.8 months and talk at 11.2 months. The results of these in-

[1] Mead, C. D. The relation of general intelligence to certain mental and physical traits. Teachers' College, Columbia University Contributions to Education, No. 76. New York City, 1916. P. 117.

[2] Terman, L. M. Genetic studies of genius, Vol. 1., Stanford University Press, 1926, pp. 186–7.

vestigators are presented in tabular form in Table 1.

TABLE 1

RELATION OF INTELLIGENCE TO AGE OF WALKING AND TALKING

Intelligence	Walking	Talking
Superior	12.8 months	11.2 months
Normal	13.5	15.8
Schoolable defectives	21.6	34.4
"Idiots"	30.0	51.0

From this table it is evident that the appearance of walking and talking is definitely related to intelligence, and that these motor activities therefore serve as criteria of growth in intelligence. Cunningham,[1] in measuring gross motor development of infants and young children, has also found a definite correlation between mental age as measured by intelligence tests and such activities as climbing, throwing, aiming and balancing. According to the intelligence tests of infants now in use, such as the Kuhlman scale, a child who is unable to balance his head or to sit up alone at the age of twelve months is said to be intellectually retarded unless there are specific physical reasons for the defect. Such a disability is clearly a lack of development of muscular coördination.

[1] Cunningham, B. V. An experiment in measuring gross motor development of infants and young children. Journal of educational psychology, 1927, 18, 458–64.

In addition to tests of motor capacity, the usual tests for progress in intelligence of the infant include immediate coördinated responses to specific sensory stimuli—turning of the head toward sound, rotation of the eyes toward light, reaching for and grasping an object. Each of these acts is an example of coördinated motor activity which has developed through a trial and error process.

The defense reactions to a noxious stimulus such as pinching of the face show how the final adaptive ability of an act depends upon the development of a coördinated response. A newborn infant first reacts by throwing about the arms, legs and head. With increase in experience, some of these movements drop out and the precision of others increases; the head is thrown back immediately as if to move away from the stimulus, and the movements of the arms become better coordinated. Chance successes occur in which the hands touch the stimulating object. Coördination further increases in precision until finally when the stimulus is applied, the head is pulled back and the hands touch the stimulus together directly in order to push it away.

Other responses which show clearly that the development of sensori-motor coördination is a growth in intelligence are those which result from the stimulation of the distance receptors. These receptors respond to stimuli which originate at some place away from the body, that is, form no actual contact with the body. The eyes and ears are distance receptors. Reaching for an object is an example of a complex response to the stimulation of a distance receptor. Many simpler coordinations are already well developed before the infant attempts to perform this intelligent act. The eye coördination must be adequate to follow and fixate the object; the musculature of the shoulders and arms must act in conjunction; the body must be balanced, etc. The final response is due to a synergic combination of all these reactions. An infant usually begins to reach out in response to a strong visual stimulus at about the fourth month, that is, when the prerequisite coördinations have been well established. No one hesitates to consider this as denoting intelligence. The simpler coördinations, such as the response to pressure or to pain, likewise measure the degree of intelligent adjustment of the infant. The reaching out of the arms in response to a visual stimulus does not develop until later than their response to pinching of the chin because it consists of a greater number of reflex responses and involves finer coördinations.

Further analysis of the intelligence tests used for increasing age levels shows that they attempt to measure the increasing complexity of the child's reaction possibilities to an increasing range of sensory stimuli. Intelligence development in infants is thus a progress in sensori-motor activity. Since growth in these activities shows continuity from the newborn infant to the young child, growth in the intelligence level may be measured in terms of their increasing complexity.

DELAYED SENSORI-MOTOR RESPONSES IN MENTALLY RETARDED CHILDREN

It is well known that a child who does not learn to sit up or to respond to visual and auditory stimuli until late in infancy proves to be mentally retarded later. The history of backward and feeble-minded children, also, usually shows that these sensori-motor coördinations have been late in appearing. The sensitivity of these children is apparently less than that of the normal child and their coördinations when they do appear are inferior. Mental retardation is a frequent accompaniment of defects in the use of muscles, such as occur in birth injuries. The resulting loss of voluntary muscular control prevents the child from learning to perform the muscular coördinations necessary for maintaining balance of the head and trunk, and the complex coördinated movements involved in manipulatory habits. Evidence of general mental retardation may also be obtained in the infant under two weeks of age. The adequacy of sensory activity and of motor coördinations at this time shows a direct correlation with future mental development.

The relationship between adequacy of sensori-motor responses and intellectual growth is illustrated in the following history of a pair of twins. The environment of these infants was closely similar and their treatment and care differed very little. When one week old the girl showed more active responses to pain and touch than the boy, and her motor coördinations of eyeballs, arms and hands were distinctly superior to his. He was very sluggish in all his reactions, showed no initiative or interest in feeding, and was also less irritable than the girl, who was more alert generally. When they were about two months of age, a light was flashed between their cribs as a test of their responsiveness; the girl quickly turned her head toward it, but the boy did not respond. She began to sit up at least eight weeks before the boy. When they were one year old, the girl began to walk with good success and spoke a few words. The boy, on the other hand, was just beginning to stand with help and did not speak at all. At eighteen months the girl talked in sentences and was very active physically, walking and running about, but the boy was not yet able to talk and was very awkward in all his movements. It was thus apparent from his responses at one week of age that the later development of the boy would be slow, as his later responses proved.

Numerous other cases might be cited in which defects in the early sensori-motor responses can be directly correlated with retarded intellectual development later on. Deaf and blind children, for example, are usually inferior to the physically normal child, according to standard tests of intelligence. They cannot advance as rapidly as others because they do not come in contact with as varied an environment; in other words, they do not receive the stimulations the child with normal sensory processes receives. Recent surveys have also shown that deaf children grade lower in intelligence than blind children, which is probably due to the fact that they are deprived of the verbal communication so essential for language development. Language symbolically takes the place of many early sensori-motor responses, and the intelligence of the deaf who do not replace their early methods of response by language does not advance as quickly as that of normal children.

Although it is possible that many infants who are retarded during the first few weeks of life may later develop in a normal manner, any retardation should be dealt with immediately by instituting intensive training of the sensori-motor responses under the direction of a skilled adviser. The psychological study of the newborn infant is as necessary a part of his routine care as close physical observation, and the failure to begin the process of stimulation early may result in defective development later. One of the important factors contributing to negligence in this regard is the attitude of many persons, including physicians, who evade the problem by saying that "the child will outgrow it" or "he will be all right later on." Neglect of the mental development of infants should be regarded as seriously as the failure to treat physical defects. From the standpoint of the infant's future welfare both factors are extremely important.

THE LEARNING PROCESS

The acquisition of a new form of response or the increase in complexity of an old method of response is designated as learning. When a new activity is being acquired the reaction is perfected for the adjustment to a specific type of stimulation. According to Professor Carr, of the Psychological Laboratory of the University of Chicago, where extensive experiments have been carried out on learning in man and animals, learning presupposes the presence of a problem, the overcoming of an obstacle to a goal the reaching of which is the solution of the problem. The opening of a puzzle box is such a problem. The animal or person is required to overcome an obstacle or barrier to the attainment of his goal, the opening of the box. Learning takes place only when the learner is persistent in his attempts to overcome the obstacle, and, failing by one sort of attack upon the problem, resorts to a variety of attacks until he finds the right one. When the obstacle is removed and the goal attained, the problem is solved. Activity then ceases and is repeated only when the identical situation is represented. Learning, then, goes on only when an individual has not yet developed a mode of behavior which will adjust him to a given stimulating condition, and when, the adjustment established, he goes on improving his adaptation to the environment.

The first sensori-motor responses of the infant may be compared to those of an animal attempting to escape from a problem box. The animal attempting to adjust to a new situation at first makes movements which are random for the particular problem. During the random activity by chance success is attained. In succeeding repetitions the particular response which solves the problem and adjusts the animal to the stimulating condition then appears earlier and earlier and the unsuccessful movements gradually drop out. The infant's first response to stimuli is also a random activity, and the adequacy of his reactions increases with the repetition of the act since the various movements which he makes become more definite and precise with practice. Most of the behavior of the growing infant is a result of such specific learning activity.

An analysis of the learning process in the formation of complex habits of skill shows that such habits develop by the progressive combination of simple units of activity into the final act. Typewriting is a good example of this fact. It requires the habit of correct finger placement, of pressing the keys, and of manipulating the fingers, all without vision. The first progress is made in learning the position of letters; then word habits are formed, such that the learner can respond in a unified way to a number of letters at one time. After these have become automatic, combinations of words are learned, and finally sentences. Thus the simple coördinations are first learned separately and then finally combined into the single complex act of typewriting, and no improvement is shown until the simple habits have become fixed.

Similarly in the child, the formation of complex habits depends upon the acquisition of simple organized acts which in turn grow out of the aimless, undifferentiated activity of the young infant. The fact that the infant is able to perform numerous aimless movements makes it possible for him to develop a great variety of habits later on. Very shortly after birth he begins to organize the aimless movements of his arms, legs, trunk and head, which form the matrix of much of his later behavior, into simple coördinated responses made at first to a single stimulus. These simple organized acts are the units out of which the complex habits that develop later are formed. At first muscle groups which are positionally near each other begin to react in a coördinated fashion. With increase in experience, the reactions become more complex in character until separated groups of muscles begin to respond in an integrated way. Coördinated activity of the arms and legs, for example, occurs only after these muscle groups have each begun to function well. Integration between the various sense organs also develops rapidly and responses are soon made to the simultaneous stimulation of two or more types of receptors. Conditioning goes on rapidly; responses first made to one type of stimulation are soon made to a substituted stimulus. Although reactions to tactual stimulation are the first to be developed, visual or auditory objects soon arouse responses.

As the child grows older the undifferentiated reactions shown by the infant no longer appear in response to stimulation, as these activities have been coördinated into definite acts by means of the learning process. When confronted with a new problem these distinctly organized acts are now brought into use instead of the earlier random activities, and are combined into more elaborate arrangements. The process of learning at this time, and of all later learning, is not different in kind, however, from the early coördination of random movements, but only in degree of complexity. The behavior of the older child is not random in the sense that the early activity of the infant is aimless and unguided, but only in the sense that it may at first fail to meet the particular situation to which adjustment is attempted.

Human behavior is composed largely of responses built up from the chaotic muscular activity which the infant first shows; through practice these responses are quickly changed into simple coördinated acts, which in turn are combined into highly complex muscular activities. From the time of birth and probably before, the infant begins to develop a large number of habits. The first habits learned are those dealing with responses to simple sensory stimuli such as contact. Later, the more complex habits develop in response to stimulation of the distance receptors. In all habits the progress made is similar to that shown by the infant in the development of his early sensori-motor responses, namely, it is rapid at first and later slowly advances toward perfection.

The types of habit which are learned at any

time in an individual's life are those which his environmental "set" demands. This is especially true in the first few years of life during which the infant and child are adjusted to a limited environment. The stimuli of this environment are particularly uniform for most infants and the first habits to be formed are therefore quite universal. Nevertheless, marked differences often are observed in infants as young as two weeks of age or even earlier. By the time the age of two years is reached, many different types of habits have been formed in response to particular stimuli, making the child definitely different from every other child.

In dealing with young children the question often arises as to the number of habits that should be taught. Within the limitations of the environment, the more numerous the habits established, the better the child is able to adjust to the large number of complex stimuli which he must meet. An individual is usually characterized by the types of habit he has formed and the importance these responses have assumed in his daily adjustment.

The function of habits is to increase the number of reactions an individual can make and to increase skill in particular acts so that they can be performed quickly and with the fewest possible errors. As efficiency in any particular act is increased, the amount of effort necessary to carry out the act is decreased, so that more activities can develop in response to new situations, enabling the individual constantly to widen his environment and become better adjusted to it.

Learning what not to do is an important part of the learning process, which takes place chiefly through the elimination of errors. Numerous experiments have been carried out upon animals and human beings to determine the effect of guidance upon learning, and in many cases it has been found that learning takes place more quickly and more thoroughly when guidance is not given. Some of these experiments have shown that guidance if limited in amount may be an aid when introduced early in the learning process, but that too much guidance, or guidance that is instituted late, is actually detrimental. When given early, it prevents the development of non-useful habits and encourages helpful ones, but when given late it may be confusing rather than beneficial. These results have a direct relation to children's learning and their ability to meet new situations. Usually children are hampered by too much guidance in their learning processes. As a result they become too dependent upon it and fail to develop the initiative necessary for meeting new problems.

THE DEVELOPMENT OF SPEECH AS A CONTINUATION OF SENSORI-MOTOR RESPONSES

The newborn infant adjusts to the environment by means of sensori-motor responses which *are* his intelligence, since intelligence is defined as the ability to adjust to new situations. Sensori-motor development in infants is not only an indicator of the growth of intelligence, but is in reality that growth in its early manifestations.

Many of the sensori-motor responses become fully coördinated and integrated quite early and so are not capable of further development. A new method of utilizing these reactions must then be developed in order that the intelligence of the child may increase. Combinations of muscular movements appear. Muscular responses cannot continue to increase in complexity indefinitely, however, because of the limitations of the structure of the organism. A point is reached where various sensori-motor responses and their combinations do not suffice to adjust the child quickly.

At this point symbols take the place of many reactions—in other words, speech begins. By the use of language numerous reactions can be combined and highly complex forms of behavior developed with less effort and in less time than is taken by the sensori-motor responses by which the child must deal with the environment directly.

Speech is a far quicker method of response than gross bodily activity. It also provides a much finer means of adjustment than the slower and more cumbersome activity of the arms, legs and trunk, and is effective where an adjustment with the larger musculature would be impossible. Once the use of language is developed a large part of behavior is carried out by means of speech habits.

When intelligence begins to develop by the use of language symbols, it can no longer be measured as directly as by the measurement of sensori-motor responses. For this reason scales of intelligence of the child older than one year are an indirect measure, whereas those for the younger infant are direct measures, based upon estimations of the infant's sensori-motor activity. Tests involving language also differ from direct measurements such as height or weight in that the criterion of intelligence is based upon what the child has already learned. The use of such tests to indicate the growth of intelligence rests upon the assumption that inherent ability can be inferred from what has been learned, the relation between the amount learned and the age of the child giving the examiner a clue as to the abilities of the child.

The first speech to develop consists almost entirely of nouns. Then verbs appear, and finally adjectives, adverbs and other parts of speech. It is by means of adjectives that the child first begins to qualify objects. Before adjectives appear in his speech, his intelligence is not sufficient to enable him to make distinctions between the various qualities of objects.

A study of the language development of the child shows that the ability to qualify responses increases with age, experience and intelligence. Symbols are developed not only to take the place of highly complex bodily activities, but also to express fine differences in objects which cannot be expressed by such activities. Language, and especially the adjective, enables the individual to indicate qualitative differences in objects which it would otherwise be impossible to communicate.

The growth curve of language symbols is similar to that of all sensori-motor responses. When these responses are delayed, as in the mentally defective child, language also is late in its appearance and development. This is a further indication that language is a symbolic replacement and continuation of the early sensori-motor responses. Not only does language appear later in mentally defective than in normal children, but its development is also slower, so that the use of verbs, adjectives and the combination of words into phrases does not appear until some time after nouns have been put into use.

The relationship between sensori-motor ability

and intelligence as measured in terms of language symbols is also seen in the superior sensori-motor skill of children of superior intelligence. Sometimes the performance ability of a child is relatively better than his mental ability as measured by intelligence tests, but in these cases it is usually found that the child comes from a home either where a foreign language is spoken or where the language standards are poor.

This relationship is also apparent in habit formation. The individual who is defective in general intelligence not only is often backward in the development of speech but also finds it impossible to learn difficult habits of skill.

Chapter V

THE OBSERVATION OF THE EMOTIONS

DIFFERENTIATION OF EMOTIONAL RESPONSES BY OBSERVERS

MOST people believe that they are able to differentiate between the various emotions [1] of infants. But when large groups of observers are shown motion pictures of the behavior of normal infants in response to various stimuli, they do not agree in naming the emotions shown. A group of graduate students in psychology saw only the reactions of infants to four types of stimuli—namely, hunger, sudden dropping through a distance of two to three feet towards a table, restraint of the head and face, and pricking with a needle on the face—the stimuli producing these reactions having been deleted from the film. They had been instructed to observe carefully the various reactions of the infants, such as arm, leg and body movements, facial expression and the duration of crying. Nevertheless they named nine different emotions for the four responses (table 2). For the

[1] For definition of an emotional response see p. 144.

hunger reaction, 13 of the 32 observers named anger, 7 named hunger, 7 fear, and so on. For the response to dropping, which presumably produces

TABLE 2

JUDGMENTS OF GRADUATE STUDENTS IN PSYCHOLOGY TO MOTION PICTURES OF THE EMOTIONAL RESPONSES OF INFANTS

Judgments	Stimuli not shown					Stimuli shown				
	Hunger	Dropping	Restraint	Needle prick	Total	Hunger	Dropping	Restraint	Needle prick	Total
Anger	13	15	16	9	53	15	5	29	13	62
Fear	7	5	5	9	26		27	4	7	38
Hunger	7	6	2	2	17	7				7
Pain	3	3	4	3	13	2	2	1	13	18
Grief	1	1		1	3					
Consternation	1	1			2					
Discomfort			2		2	6				6
Anger with fear							4	1	1	6
Anger or pain						1		1	3	5
Negative						1	1	1	1	4
Discontent						2		1		3
Doubtful							1	1	1	3
None				1	1	2				2
Irritation						1		1		2
Sleepiness			1		1					
Nausea	1				1					
Excitement							1			1
Disgust						1				1
Pain with fear							1			1
Surprise							1			1
Resistance to restraint								1		1
Anxiety						1				1
Hate									1	1
Restiveness						1				1
Repulsion									1	1
Suffocating								1		1
Total [1]	32	32	30	25	119	40	43	42	41	166

[1] The totals are not the same because not all observers made judgments of each reaction.

fear, 15 judgments of anger were given, and only 5 of fear. For the response to pricking with a needle, only 3 judgments of pain were given, 9 naming fear and 9 anger. Although a fairly large percentage of the observers named anger for the reaction following restraint, an almost equal percentage also named anger for the reaction following dropping.

Another group of students who were shown motion pictures of a number of emotional reactions of infants, and were told specifically that they would see only four different types of response, namely, hunger due to a deferred feeding period, fear aroused by sudden dropping, anger resulting from light restraint of the head, and pain due to pricking with a needle, had no better success in naming the emotions shown than the observers who were not told how many and which emotions they would see. Only 10 percent of these observers named the hunger response correctly, 49 percent calling it pain, 26 percent anger and 15 percent fear (table 3). For the response to pricking with a needle, the most frequent estimate was fear; anger was considered to typify this reaction just as often as pain. Although for the response to dropping, fear was named more frequently than any other emotion, this estimate was made by 30 percent of the observers only, 27 percent (statistically a negligible difference) calling it anger. The response to restraint was detected more "successfully" than any of the others, 31 percent naming it correctly, although in all 69 percent failed to detect anger in it, 23 percent calling it pain.

Thus it is evident that observers have difficulty in recognizing the character of emotional reactions and in differentiating between them; and also that there is little correspondence between observers' judgments of the emotional responses of infants and the reactions generally expected to result from specific types of stimuli.

TABLE 3

JUDGMENTS OF STUDENTS IN PSYCHOLOGY OF MOTION PICTURES OF THE EMOTIONAL RESPONSES OF INFANTS, WHEN TOLD THE NUMBER AND TYPE OF EMOTIONS THEY WOULD SEE.

	Judgments					
	Hunger	Pain	Anger	Fear	Don't know	Total
Stimulus			Percent			
"Hunger"	10	49	26	15		100
Needle prick	18	20	20	33	9	100
Restraint	18	23	31	18	10	100
Dropping	21	19	27	30	3	100

When, however, observers endeavor to guess the types of stimuli which have produced the responses they have attempted to name, the stimuli they list correspond closely with those which are generally expected to result in the particular emotional reactions. Most students of psychology, for example, learn that fear follows dropping or a loud noise, and accordingly when they label a particular emotional response as fear they assume that the stimulus which caused it was one of these. Although only four different stimuli were employed in a certain test, the observers, who were not told how many types of reactions they would see, listed fifteen different stimuli as probably used (table 4). When they named fear, 20 of 26 observers gave either dropping or a loud noise as the

TABLE 4

ESTIMATES BY GRADUATE STUDENTS IN PSYCHOLOGY OF THE PROBABLE STIMULUS PRODUCING EMOTIONAL REACTIONS.

Probable stimulus [1]	Emotion named								
	Hunger	Anger	Sleepiness	Consternation	Fear	Pain	Nausea	Discomfort	Total
Pain		29			4	5			38
Preventing free movements		16							16
Dropping		1			10				11
Hunger	6	1				3	1		11
Loud noise					10				10
Food removed	4	5							9
Intense light						2			2
Uncomfortable clothes								2	2
Sees something	1								1
Bitter taste				2					2
Sight of bottle	1								1
Bandaged arm		1							1
Fear					1				1
Awakened from sleep			1						1
Someone said "Boo"					1				1
Total [1]	12	53	1	2	26	10	1	2	107

[1] Not all observers estimated the probable cause for each emotion named.

probable cause; for the pain reaction, they gave either pain, hunger or intense light; for the hunger reaction, hunger, removal of food, sight of bottle, etc. These results show the influence of predetermined notions regarding the reactions which specific stimuli arouse. Of those who named anger as one of the emotional responses observed, only 17 gave restraint as the probable cause, 29 naming pain, which shows again the effect of definite attitudes concerning the causes of emotions.

THE INFLUENCE OF KNOWLEDGE OF THE STIMULUS UPON JUDGMENTS OF OBSERVERS

Even when observers of motion pictures of the emotional responses of infants also see the stimuli which produced the responses, they cannot agree in their estimates of the emotions, and give a wide variety of names for the reactions seen. Nevertheless their judgments in these cases correspond more closely with the emotions ordinarily expected to follow certain types of stimulation than when they do not see the stimuli. For example, the response to dropping they most frequently judged as fear (table 2); for restraint, the most common estimate was anger. Of the group who did not see the infant dropped, 16 percent named fear as the emotion shown, whereas of those who did, 63 percent named fear. For the reaction following restraint, 53 percent of the first group and 69 percent of the second named anger. For the response to pricking with a needle 12 percent of the first group and 32 percent of the second named pain. The hunger response, curiously enough, was actually detected less well when the observers were told that the child had not been fed than when they did not know the stimulating conditions, only 7 naming hunger while 15 named anger. Again, although 13 observers named pain for the reaction following pricking with a needle, an equal number named anger. Nevertheless it is evident that in the majority of cases knowledge of the stimulus influences the observer's ability to differentiate the emotional responses of infants.

When the motion pictures are arranged so that the emotional responses of infants are shown preceded by stimuli other than those which actually produced the reactions, a marked influence is noted upon the judgments of observers, which also goes to show that they are not based solely upon observed differences in the infants' responses, but are influenced by a knowledge of differences in the stimuli which have aroused the reactions. In one such test the observers, a group of medical students, were asked to note carefully the activity of the infants, such as movements of the arms, legs and body, movements of the head, the duration and apparent intensity of crying, and the manner of breathing, and to base their estimate of the emotions shown upon this behavior. Considerable lack of agreement was evidenced in differentiating and naming the responses. For the hunger reaction, which was shown following pricking with a needle, 60 percent of the observers (table 5) named pain, but no one named hunger; for the reaction

TABLE 5

JUDGMENTS OF MEDICAL STUDENTS TO MOTION PICTURES OF EMOTIONAL RESPONSES OF INFANTS

Stimuli producing the reactions

	"Hunger"	Dropping	Restraint	Needle prick
	Stimuli shown observers				
Judgments	Needle prick	Restraint	Dropping	"Hunger"	Total
Anger	6	13	7		26
Fear	2	4	14		20
Pain	15	3			18
Hunger				17	17
Discomfort		2		3	5
Pain or fear	1	1	2		4
Irritation	1	3			4
Pain or anger		2	1		3
Gastric pain				2	2
Intestinal colic				1	1
Grief		1			1
Surprise			1		1
Resistance		1			1
Total [1]	25	30	25	23	103

[1] Not all observers made estimates of each reaction.

following dropping (presumably producing fear) which actually was shown following restraint, 43 percent named anger, the emotion one would expect to result from restraint; for the reaction following restraint, which was shown following dropping, 56 percent named fear, and only half that many named anger; and for the response following pricking with a needle, which was shown following a blank portion of film denoting a deferred feeding period, 74 percent named hunger, but not one named pain. These observers were thus greatly influenced by the stimuli shown. Although they were specifically instructed to make their decisions upon the actual activity of the infants, their naming of the emotions was most frequently determined not by the actual reactions of the infant, but by the stimuli preceding the reactions.

Everyone is liable to error in judging the emotional expressions of infants. The reasons given by the observers in Table 2 (stimulus shown) for naming the reactions as they did are significant in accounting for their judgments. Many of them stated that they were able to name the various emotions because they were influenced either by seeing the stimuli given or by a knowledge of previous work in which it was found that certain stimuli give rise to certain definite emotional responses. Some said that they named the emotions according to the way *they* would feel if the same stimuli were given to them. In estimating the emotional behavior of infants, people tend to read into it their own attitudes towards the expected reaction, and each one makes his judgment on the assumption that since he himself reacts in a particular way to certain stimuli, infants must behave in a similar manner. Frequently we ascribe to the child reactions of which he is not at all capable. If we believe that the emotions are native characteristics with a predetermined pattern, we are very likely to attribute to the child emotional reactions which in reality may be merely attempts to adjust with the body as a whole to some stimulating condition. The infant even as old as six months does not show typical forms of behavior which can be characterized as definite emotions, but only generally aimless responses which can at most be called vaguely adaptive. It is only after the child begins to have knowledge of the social significance of his behavior that any of his responses can be named as definitely emotional. They have then become differentiated as a result of the formation of habitual methods of reaction which he utilizes in adjusting to specific situations arousing activity of the body as a whole.

Our judgments of the emotions of adults, although often based upon more definite behavior, also are influenced to a great extent by a knowledge of the environmental circumstances. The adult may show few evidences of emotional reactions, and yet if we know the situation which has produced his response we do not hesitate to label it as some particular emotion. The recent experimental studies made by Landis [1] indicated little correspondence between subjects' reports of the emotions they experienced in response to a wide variety of stimuli and their facial expressions as recorded by camera and motion pictures. When they tried voluntarily to register various emotions they gave the traditional expressions and not those actually obtained in emotional situations. Landis points out that observers viewing such pictures really make their judgments on the basis of their past experience with illustrated portraits and the like which have had labels attached to them naming the emotion, and not on the basis of similarities between the expressions and those that ordinarily occur.

THE INFLUENCE OF TRAINING ON JUDGMENTS OF OBSERVERS

Training in psychology tends to make observers cautious in attempting to differentiate and name the emotional reactions of infants, even when they know the types of stimulation to which the infants have been subjected. This can be seen by comparing the estimates of a group of Normal School

[1] Landis, C. Studies of emotional reactions. I. Journal of experimental psychology, 1924, 7, 325-42. II. Journal of comparative psychology, 1924, 4, 447-509.

freshmen with those of graduate students in psychology when both were shown motion pictures of infants. The majority of the Normal School students had had but one course in psychology, and a small number had had no formal work in that subject. The film was first shown with the stimulating conditions deleted, and then both the stimuli and the reactions were shown.

Normal School students, like graduate students in psychology, showed little agreement in naming the emotions when the stimuli producing the reactions were not known. They named sixteen different emotions for the four types of response seen, and little correspondence was evident between the emotions named and those generally expected to result from the types of stimuli given.

When the stimuli were shown to these students together with the reactions, the number of "correct" responses was much greater than when they did not see the stimuli, with one exception—the graduate students actually were less successful in naming the hunger reaction when they knew the stimulus than when they did not. In comparing the improvement of the two groups, it is evident (table 6) that in all cases the Normal School students do much better. This may indicate a greater degree of caution in the more highly trained observers, or it may show that less trained observers make more use of their knowledge of the stimulus producing an emotional reaction. It certainly shows that a knowledge of psychology and of experimental studies of emotion does not aid graduate students materially in differentiating various emotional reactions of infants.

TABLE 6

THE INFLUENCE OF TRAINING ON JUDGMENTS OF EMOTIONAL RESPONSES

Percent naming emotion "correctly"
Graduate students in psychology Norman School freshmen

Reactions	Stimuli not shown	Stimuli shown	Stimuli not shown	Stimuli shown
Hunger	22	18	26	38
Fear	16	63	16	70
Anger	53	69	31	54
Pain	12	32	36	67

Effects of Interests and Attitudes upon Judgments of Observers

The marked difference in the type of judgment given by students of psychology and by medical students and nurses indicates that differences in interests and attitudes, and the consequent vocabulary, determine in part the names they give to particular reactions. The students both of psychology and medicine were familiar with the results of studies of the emotions of infants, but the former had had more training in academic psychology. They named "anger" most frequently, but the medical students and nurses named "colic" most often, although they named "fear" and "anger" almost as many times. Medical students and nurses look for some organic condition to account for the behavior of the infant; the student of psychology, knowing that he is to estimate an emotional response, looks for signs of an emotion that he believes occurs or that he knows has already been studied. The vocabulary of the former also relates more frequently to some physical condition, whereas the vocabulary of the latter contains more specific terms for emotions than that of most people not trained in psychology.

Observation of nurses working in the nursery shows the same effect of their training upon their judgments. If a nurse hears an infant crying after feeding time, she is likely to attribute the crying to illness, probably colic, or to being awakened from sleep, since the child has been fed and cannot be hungry. Her decision is made on the basis of probability and not upon any definite behavior characteristics of the infant, even when she is instructed to note the type and duration of crying, arm and leg movements, and other activities of the child. Although ordinarily confident they can name the emotional reactions of infants easily, when tested nurses hesitate to make decisions concerning infants' emotional responses, and almost always want to know what has happened to the infant before giving an opinion. A very small percentage make "correct" judgments.

The motion picture method of presenting the reactions of infants to observers is necessarily limited because certain aspects of the reactions are not visible, such as flushing or paling of the skin, changes in breathing, and the character of the cry. These sensory data should furnish additional clues in estimating emotional reactions if they occur in any consistent manner in the different emotions.

Medical students and student nurses were taken into the nursery in small groups and shown the actual behavior of infants who were stimulated in various ways to bring out supposedly definite emotions. They were told to observe the infants very carefully, as the reactions would be of comparatively short duration. Their attention was called particularly to movements of the arms, legs and body, the type and duration of the cry, the facial expression and any change in breathing. Immediately after the stimulus was applied, a screen which hid the infant from view was removed and the observers were allowed to watch its behavior. The screen was then replaced, another infant stimulated in a different way, and the observers again

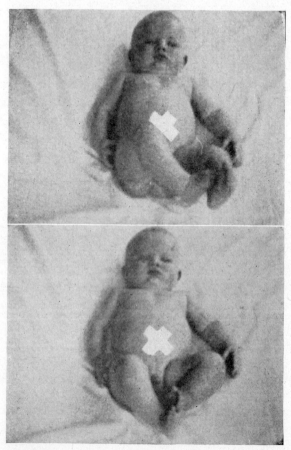

Fig. 8.   A normal six month infant at rest.

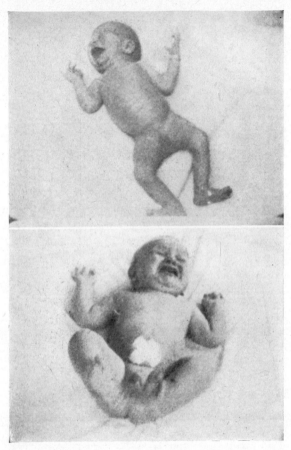

Fig. 9. Response of a four-day-old and a six month old infant to pricking with a needle. Can you tell what emotion they show—do you see any difference between their reactions?

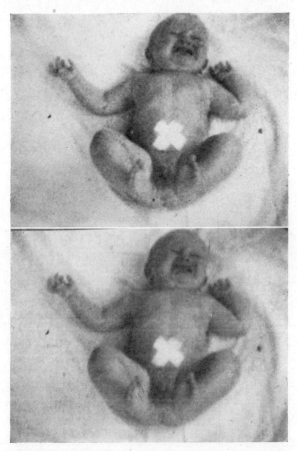

Fig. 10. This seven-day-old was dropped about
three feet. What does he show?

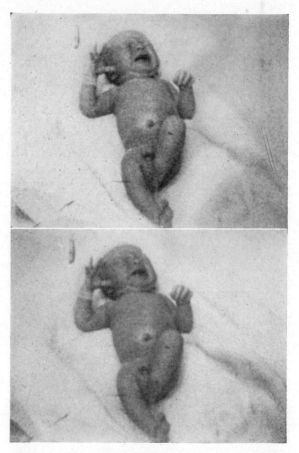

Fig. 11. Any sudden stimulation causes a marked reaction in a young infant. In this case a sudden draft was produced on the face by means of a rubber bag.

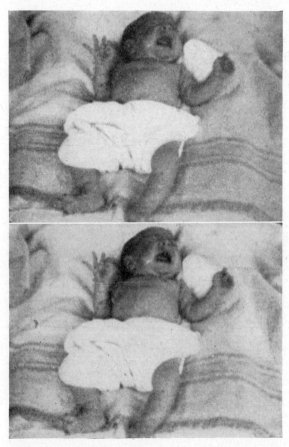

Fig. 12. This six-week-old was suffering from colic. Is this reaction different from those produced by the other stimuli?

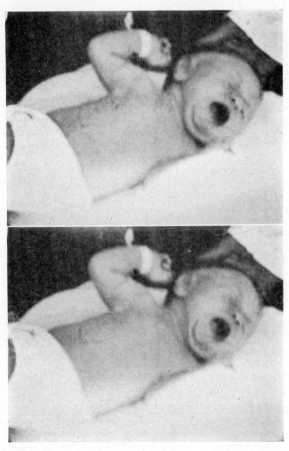

Fig. 13. This infant's movements have just been restrained. Anger is supposed to result. Can you identify it?

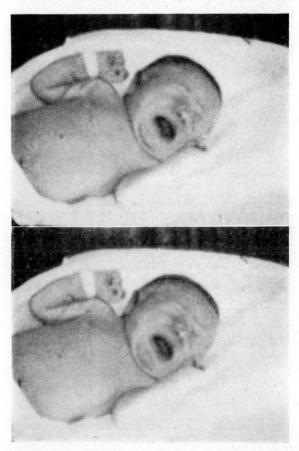

Fig. 14. Thirty minutes past feeding time!

Fig. 15.   Ingenuity and social adaptability are stimulated by directed group activity.

noted the reaction. All the infants observed were between 112 and 160 hours old.

Nine different emotions were named for the three reactions shown (table 7). The judgment most frequently given was colic; then in order of frequency came fear, anger, hunger, pain, and so on. The reaction following dropping of the infant was most frequently estimated as colic, four observers only naming fear. The reaction following restraint was estimated as anger, the emotion ordinarily expected to result, only by four, seventeen naming fear. Ten observers estimated pain as typifying the response to pricking with a needle, but an equal number named anger. There is thus no agreement between observers in estimating emotional reactions to stimuli which presum-

TABLE 7

JUDGMENTS IN THE NURSERY BY MEDICAL STUDENTS AND NURSES OF THE EMOTIONAL RESPONSES OF INFANTS WHEN THE STIMULI WERE NOT SEEN

| | Stimulus | | | |
Judgments	Dropping	Restraint	Needle prick	Total
Colic	13	9	4	26
Fear	4	17	3	24
Anger	8	4	10	22
Hunger	8	4	4	16
Pain	4	2	10	16
Awakened from sleep	11	2	1	14
Organic brain emotion	1	7	3	11
Tight bandage	1	3	2	6
Uncomfortable	2		1	3
Total [1]	52	48	38	138

[1] Totals are not the same because not all observers made estimates of each reaction shown.

ably arouse a given emotion, even when they see and hear the infants' responses, which shows that these reactions are not those generally expected.

Effect of the Cry upon Observers

The character of the crying of an infant often is used as an aid in judging the emotion which it shows. It is ordinarily assumed that the cry differs in different emotions and that such differences may be detected easily. However, when variations are heard, they can be shown to be due to differences in the intensity, duration and manner of application of the stimulus arousing the cry rather than to any intrinsic differences in the character of the cry in different emotions. (See Chapter VI).

Many observers shown motion picture views of the emotional reactions of infants think they would be aided in judging the emotional character of the responses if they also could hear the crying of the child. Groups who watched the actual reactions of infants in the nursery, however, showed no better success in their estimates than those who only saw motion pictures of the responses. As these observers stated that they were watching the bodily movements of the infants, and did not direct their attention to the nature of the cry, groups of from two to five—graduate students in psychology, medical students and nurses—were taken into the nursery and stationed in front of a screen behind which an infant was placed upon a table and stimulated. The screen was not withdrawn, but after the crying of the infant had subsided, the observers were asked to write the name of the emotion which it denoted, and their reasons for giving that particular name. In order that the judgments should be based on the quality of the cry, and not upon its duration, the infants were removed from the room after about two minutes, unless the cry subsided in a shorter time.

Considerable lack of agreement was shown by these observers (table 8). Ten different emotions were named for the responses to four types of stim-

TABLE 8

JUDGMENTS OF THE EMOTIONAL CHARACTER OF THE CRYING OF INFANTS

	Stimulus				
Judgments	"Hunger"	Dropping	Restraint	Needle prick	Total
Colic	4	7	3	2	16
Hunger	6	2	2	5	15
Pain		3	5	5	13
Anger	2	6	2	1	11
Fear	3	1	4		8
Awakened from sleep	1		3	4	8
Irritation			3	1	4
Sleepiness	2	2			4
Discomfort		1		1	2
Grief	1		1		2
Total [1]	19	22	23	19	83

[1] The totals are not the same because not all observers made estimates of each reaction.

uli, the most frequent being colic, hunger, pain and anger. For the cry following a delayed feeding period, only 6 observers named hunger, and 5 gave the same name to the reaction following a needle prick. Fear was named only once as characterizing the cry which followed dropping. For the cry following restraint of the head, presumably arousing anger, only 2 named anger, 4 naming fear and 5 pain. For the cry following pricking with a needle 5 named pain, but an equal number named hunger. There is thus little relation between judgments of the emotional character of an infant's crying and the emotion generally expected to result from a given type of stimulation.

Observers who hear the crying of the infant name "colic" much more frequently than when they base their observation only upon motion picture views. Not one judgment of "colic" was made by the students of psychology who saw the motion pictures, and only 3 percent of the medical students named colic or gastric pain. When both groups made estimates of the cries of infants, however, 19 percent named "colic." This estimate was given more often than "anger" or "fear," whereas in observing motion pictures, "anger" and "fear" were named more often than any other emotion. The crying of infants is thus very likely to suggest an organic disturbance.

When allowed to listen to the cry of an infant

during its entire duration, after application of a stimulus, observers show a tendency to judge a cry which is prolonged over two or three minutes, and which subsides and increases rhythmically in intensity, as that of hunger. In general, this judgment proves correct. When crying is unusually long and intermittent, subsiding and recurring with sudden intensity, it usually is estimated as "colic." Again, a cry which is sharp, loud and of short duration usually is judged as that of anger or cutaneous pain. The fact that, in general, observers name hunger or colic correctly when allowed to listen to an infant's crying for more than two minutes, but are unable to judge the character of the cry of a shorter period, indicates that these judgments result from the association of prolonged crying with some organic condition. Mothers, when unable to find any other cause for a child's prolonged crying, usually attribute it to hunger, pain or some other organic condition. This is also true of nurses.

Although most mothers believe that they can recognize the emotional character of the cry of their infants, they probably base their decisions upon a knowledge of the causative conditions producing the infant's reaction rather than upon the quality of the cry. The mother first looks at her child to see if he is hurt in any way, then she looks for pins which may be sticking him, looks at his clothing to see if it is too tight, and then perhaps observes the time of day to decide whether he is hungry. When the infant cries during or just preceding the usual feeding time she is likely to regard his reaction as due to hunger. In young infants the character of the cry during an emotional reaction is thus dependent not so much upon the type of emotional response as upon the character of the stimulating conditions arousing the reaction. In older infants and children, however, an additional factor is introduced which aids the parent in recognizing the emotional character of their cry. It becomes fairly definite in some situations, and the parent associates a given cry with a specific stimulus and attributes it to that stimulus.

CONCLUSION

Most persons judge the emotional behavior of an individual in terms of the stimuli which have produced the reactions. They have learned the names of a number of emotions and have learned to evaluate various emotional responses in terms of the stimulating conditions which have aroused them. If the situation confronting an individual is estimated to be one which arouses an aggressive reaction, the resulting response is named "anger," but if it is considered dangerous to his welfare, the response will be called "fear." In this way the differentiation of emotions is based upon a knowledge of the character of the stimulating circumstances rather than upon differences in overt behavior. It is true that when differences in responses are marked, the reactions themselves also influence these judgments. If attempted escape by running away occurs in response to a stimulus, most persons ascribe the reaction to fear; if fighting results, the behavior is estimated as anger. Decisions concerning the adult's emotional reactions, however, are based primarily upon the stimulating circumstances, because his emotions are not manifested as overtly as those of children, owing to his greater control of his emotional reactions.

The development of criteria for differentiation between various emotions is important for the clinician as well as the experimental investigator. Further discussion of the nature and function of these responses will be found in the next chapter.

Chapter VI

THE NATURE OF THE EMOTIONS AND THEIR INFLUENCE UPON BEHAVIOR

THE NATURE AND FUNCTION OF EMOTIONAL RESPONSES

AN emotional response, like any other, serves to adjust the individual to some stimulating condition; but it differs from other types of response in that it involves a massive, unpremeditated reaction of the entire body. This sort of attempt at adaptation is most clearly observed in young children, since the outward manifestations of their emotional reactions have not yet been suppressed by training. In adults it often is difficult to see how emotional responses serve the process of adaptation because experience has changed the patterns of their reactions.

The term "instinctive" has often been employed to describe much of the behavior of newborn infants, and attempts have been made to indicate its "purposive" nature. But we have seen that their first reactions to most simple sensory stimuli are undifferentiated and only with experience do their movements become quite specific in relation to the particular stimulating condition. Any form of *sudden* stimulation, such as dropping, loud noises, restraint, pain, or a rush of air on the face, produces in the young infant aimless activity of most of the musculature, accompanied by crying. The stimuli must be sufficiently strong, however, to produce a reaction. When an infant below four or five days of age is dropped one or two feet it frequently shows no perceptible response, except for occasional vague movements of the arms and legs. The younger the infant the stronger must be the stimulus. This is also true for so-called "pleasurable" stimuli, such as stroking or petting, to which many newborn infants show no overt reaction.

Out of this matrix of undifferentiated behavior the clearly adaptive emotional responses develop. What we call the emotions, therefore, are not present in the infant at birth, but develop, as a result of experience, as specific patterns of response. The infant does show certain types of reaction, such as passivity, aggressiveness, and withdrawal, which later, as the child learns to differentiate between various situations, and establishes different responses to them, we call emotions. But this development begins immediately after birth with the handling of the child, who eventually learns to respond with specific emotional reactions because of the training he receives.

The bodily movements made during an emotional response, although more diffuse and widespread than in simple sensory responses, are also directed toward an adjustment to the specific stimulus. When restraint, for example, is applied to the head, the movements of the head and arms are much more vigorous than those of the legs, and are directed towards the removal of the noxious stimulus; whereas, when the restraint is applied to the legs, the movements of the legs are much more active than those of the head and arms. The initial response, in other words, occurs in the part stimulated and spreads to other parts of the body. But the spread of these movements occurs so quickly that unless closely observed they will appear only as a generalized activity of the entire body, especially of the arms and legs.

A great variety of stimuli, if sufficiently strong, will result in this generalized activity of the body, often accompanied by holding of the breath and spasmodic crying. A simple stimulus such as the stroking of the plantar surface of the foot will produce a flexion of the toes without much spread of muscular activity from the foot itself. But if the stroking is done with some force or is repeated several times, the foot and then the leg will be moved. If it is repeated say, eight or ten times in rapid succession, the infant will kick with both legs, wave the arms, turn the head about, and cry.

If the stroking is continued further, the crying and general activity become more intense, and the child begins to breathe spasmodically. A similar response may be brought about by continued squeezing of the infant's foot, by continued pressure on the leg, or by continued successive stimulations with a needle. The behavior in response to these various stimuli is so similar that it is impossible to designate it as a definite emotion in each case, except on the basis of the stimulus.

So-called "pleasurable" responses also may be ascribed to the adaptive activity necessary in making a response to particular types of stimuli. The usual reaction to situations which are expected to produce such responses is a passive state. The adaptive response to feeding or patting is a relaxation of the body. This is accompanied by a lessening of the tone or tension of the muscles. Faint smiling observed in very young infants may be the result of this relaxation in the facial muscles. Active smiling develops later, and is soon conditioned to appear at the sight of the mother or nurse who strokes, pats or otherwise soothes the child.

All the emotional responses of newborn infants possess the characteristics of reactions necessary for adjustment to some specific stimulus. When slow motion pictures of these responses are analyzed, the following general observations hold:

In response to *restraint* the body is thrown about,

the legs are pulled up in a non-rhythmical fashion, there may be a stiffening of the body, the breath is held, and crying becomes spasmodic.

Hunger is manifested by crying and aimless movements of the arms and legs; the hands are at times thrown upward and over the head in a rotary motion, and the legs are pulled up in much the same way as in anger at restraint.

The reaction to *dropping* is shown as incoördinated movements of the arms and legs, and a throwing of the arms above the head, such as occur in hunger, with a pulling up of the legs in a manner similar to that shown in both hunger and anger. Spreading of the fingers and clutching movements of the hands are seen, and the child screams with gusto, although at times the breath may be held as in anger.

When an infant is *pricked* with a needle several times in succession, he gives a start, makes clutching movements with the fingers, stiffens his body, moves his legs up and down, and alternately screams and holds his breath, as in fear.

DIFFERENCES IN RESPONSES CAUSED BY QUANTITATIVE ASPECTS OF THE STIMULUS

Differences in the emotional responses of infants to various types of stimuli do occur, notwithstanding the fact that, as we have seen in Chapter V, observers generally cannot differentiate consistently between them. These differences, however, are due not to the quality, but to the *quantity*—i. e. intensity and duration—of the stimulus.

In infants about two weeks of age it is possible to obtain various kinds of adaptive reactions when a given type of stimulus is varied in intensity. Thus if restraint is applied lightly to the face for a short period it produces movements of the arms and head without crying, but if applied suddenly and with intensity the response is characterized by violent kicking, pushing movements of the hands, and crying. Although the character of the response following restraint of the face does not differ markedly from the reaction that results from pricking the face with a needle, if the intensity or duration of either of these stimuli is varied, the resulting reactions differ noticeably. The differences, however, if the stimuli are applied to the same part of the body, are manifest only in the intensity and duration of the response. A conclusion regarding a real difference in the responses to two types of stimuli, therefore, can be made only when these stimuli have the same quantitative value. Furthermore, certain stimuli which appear at first hand different in character may in reality produce the same type of response in the newborn infant. For example, it is possible that a loud, shrill sound actually stimulates pain nerve endings, just as pricking with a needle does, and that the resulting reaction may be due to this painful stimulation. If so, differences between the reactions to a harsh, loud sound and to pricking with a needle may arise as a result of differences in the duration or intensity of the two painful stimuli, rather than as a direct result of the quality of each stimulus.

The quantitative aspect of a stimulus is indeed the most important factor influencing the character of the reaction which follows. Bodily movements such as raising and lowering the arms, flexion and extension of the legs, and movements of the trunk and head usually are directly proportional in their rate and duration to the strength of the stimulating condition. Spasmodic breathing and holding of the breath, so often described as characteristic of certain emotions only, are also related to the intensity and duration of the stimulus. This is illustrated in the reaction to pricking with a needle. When this stimulus is applied lightly and is repeated but once or twice an infant usually only puckers its lips and perhaps cries for a few seconds, but when applied with some intensity and repeated quickly several times loud spasmodic crying occurs, with holding of the breath between the periods of crying.

*Effect of the Quantitative Aspect of the Stimulus
as Illustrated by Variations in Character
of the Crying of Infants*

When a mildly painful stimulus is applied to a young infant the cry is neither as intense nor as prolonged as when the same type of stimulus is given with greater intensity. The character and duration of the cry are also related to the bodily movements made by the child. When a stimulus produces a great amount of bodily activity, the cry is more intense and continues longer than when bodily activity is slight. Such activity, however, probably is a function of the intensity of the stimulus, and so is related only indirectly to the cry. In general, the more intense the stimulating condition, the sharper is the ensuing cry. When a painful stimulus is applied with little intensity, the cry which follows is low-pitched and of short duration, but when applied with intensity, it begins suddenly, is of longer duration, and high-pitched in quality. The character of the cry is also related to its duration; within limits, the greater the duration of the cry the more intense it tends to become. The cry of hunger furnishes a good example of this relationship. The cry of a hungry infant observed within a period of thirty minutes following the usual feeding time begins gradually, is intermittent, and increases slowly in intensity. The intervals of quiet become less frequent with the lapse of time, and the cry following them begins more suddenly and with greater intensity than during the first few minutes.

The duration of an infant's crying increases with the continuation of the stimulating conditions. For example, the length of the crying following restraint for ten seconds is invariably greater than that following restraint for three seconds, although the increase is not proportional to the increase in duration of the stimulus. The average duration of the cry of a number of infants following restraint for ten seconds was found to be 20.2 seconds, and for restraint for three seconds, 9.6 seconds.

The manner of application of a stimulus also influences the character of the ensuing cry. When needle pricks are applied gradually, the cry of the infant begins relatively slowly and increases quickly to its full intensity. When the pricks are applied suddenly and in quick succession, however, the cry begins after a brief latent period, and reaches its greatest intensity at the outset. The cry following sudden and very firm restraint of the face is more sudden, more intense and higher in pitch than that following gradual restraint. In the latter, there usually is a relatively long latent period, and the intensity of the ensuing cry increases gradually. If the restraint is continued the cry soon changes in character to the type of cry which follows almost immediately as a result of sudden and very firm restraint.

A comparison of the hunger cry of most infants with that of infants ill with colic also illustrates the influence of the suddenness and intensity of the stimulating conditions. The crying of normal infants observed just before feeding time usually is rhythmical in character, dying down gradually, beginning again after a short interval, and gradually rising to its greatest intensity. In only a few infants is the hunger cry sudden or spasmodic. In infants with gastro-intestinal disturbance, on the other hand, the cry is sudden and spasmodic, begins with great intensity, subsides relatively quickly, and is accompanied by widespread spasmodic bodily activity. Following a quiet interval of varying duration, during which the infant may whimper, the cry is resumed in a similar manner. In hunger the contractions of the stomach wall begin gradually with no acute spasms. In colic, on the other hand, the intestinal contractions are quite marked and spasmodic in character. For this reason colic produces a more intense organic stimulus than hunger, and the onset of the stimulus is also more sudden. This sudden, intense character of the stimulus in colic results in sudden, intense and high-pitched crying.

Many conditions other than the qualitative character of the stimulus influence the type of an infant's cry, and make it difficult for an observer to estimate its emotional character. We have already seen that the time of day in relation to the feeding period is a factor. The age of the infant is also a factor, although a variable one. The duration and intensity of the cry generally are not as great in infants less than twenty-four hours old as in older infants. Infants who are considered irritable and fidgety react with more intense and prolonged crying than infants considered quiet and good in the nursery. Infants who have a private nurse show greater reactivity than those who do not, for, as we have seen, the increased handling, which means an increased number of stimuli received, results in a lowering of the threshold of irritability.

The character of the bodily movements and of the cry which constitute an emotional reaction is thus dependent upon the intensity and duration of the reaction, and the character of the emotional response, therefore, may be described in quantitative terms. The emotional responses of infants below twelve days of age possess no inherent characteristics which can be noted or adequately and precisely described.

GENESIS OF SPECIFIC EMOTIONAL RESPONSES

In Children

The genesis of the specific emotional reactions of children and adults is to be found in the responses available to the infant. Although these responses are indefinite at first, even very early two types of adjustive reaction can be noted: first, that of *rejecting* a stimulus, and second, that of *accepting* a stimulus. Examples of the first type are the responses to restraint, dropping, and pricking with a needle. The reaction to these stimuli is an attempt at defense by trying to escape from or remove them, in part by throwing the arms upward above the head, by turning the head and trunk from side to side in the case of the very young infant, and definitely away from the source of the stimulus in an older one, who also makes coördinated pushing movements with the hands. Examples of the second type are the reactions to patting, rocking or feeding, by which the infant makes an adjustment adapting him to the continuance of the stimulus.

The emotional activity which serves to reject a stimulus may be divided further into two types: (1), rejection by retreat; (2), rejection by aggressive activity. The infant at birth shows predominately the first type of activity before the second; that is, in its response to a noxious stimulus it first attempts to retreat, and if this attempt at adjustment does not suffice, follows it by aggressive behavior. Retreat preceding an aggressive reaction is illustrated by the activity following restraint. When restraint is applied to the face the newborn infant attempts to pull its head and shoulders away. If the restraint is continued, aggressive movements follow, such as throwing the arms about, kicking, and turning the body from side to side. At ten or twelve days of age the infant also shows this type of reaction to restraint, except that the time during which it attempts to retreat is much shorter, and unless looked for specifically, is often not observed. The aggressive reaction which in older infants follows immediately upon the application of a noxious stimulus, without an initial period of retreat, probably is a learned response; the child has become so conditioned by the repetition of noxious stimuli that he reacts to them by immediate aggressive behavior. This conditioning of emotional responses goes on continually, and the reactions to specific stimuli are altered considerably with the increase in experience.

Definite emotional responses are developed through experience in which some particular unpremeditated mass reactions of the body are involved. When a child makes an aggressive reaction toward an object, his behavior is labeled anger and comes to signify anger to him. When he retreats from a situation, his behavior is labeled fear and comes to signify fear to him. He is told by his parents not to get angry (show aggressive behavior), or not to be frightened (show retiring behavior) and thus he comes to establish an attitude toward each type of response. He soon learns that aggressive behavior typifies anger and that retiring behavior typifies fear. In other words particular emotional responses develop out of his learning the significance of types of behavior which are then characterized as emotions.

Thus the emotions that arise depend upon the method which is utilized in the situations where the child reacts with the entire body. It will depend upon the way the child is trained which reaction he is most likely to use in a situation that necessitates generalized activity. Most children are taught to try to escape from danger, and so are likely to show fear in dangerous situations. The particular form of the emotional response is determined by the adjustment which is made. Stimuli demanding retreat become associated with fear, those requiring aggressive behavior with anger, and those requiring passivity with love. Thus the specific emotions which become typical for an individual arise out of social usage and through experience develop as habitual methods of reaction.

In Adults

The emotional responses of the adult also are characterized by an attempt to adjust to a specific stimulus. Cannon, professor of physiology at Harvard University, has shown that in both anger and fear physiological changes occur which lead to the same definite changes in blood pressure, muscular tone, heart rate, intestinal activity, and so on. An aggressive response must be accompanied by an increase in muscular tone, a strengthened heart beat and a rise in blood pressure which allow for physical exertion. Similarly, defensive fear in the form of attempted escape also must be accompanied by a comparable set of changes. Thus the organic behavior in an emotion is of the type which can be utilized in the adjustment that is being made, and which promotes the activity at the moment. Anger and fear responses, therefore, are not differentiated by the peculiar organic activity involved, nor by any specific facial expression, but on the basis of differences in the adjustment of the body as a whole in relation to the stimulating conditions. During an anger response, for example, there is an aggressive reaction toward the object that produced the reaction, involving a sudden mass activity of the body. Behavior which is termed fear is characterized by a mass reaction of retreat from a situation, and the gross bodily activity is necessarily different from that of anger, although the organic responses may be similar.

The emotional reactions of the adult usually are not as obviously manifested as those of the infant or child. He learns to control his behavior in various situations, and the overt activity which ordinarily would characterize his emotions is inhibited. He learns, for example, to suppress his reactions in a public place, or in a situation which may involve future detrimental consequences. Further, his emotional responses have become so modified that circumstances which during childhood produced a particular emotional response may later result in a totally different reaction. The emotional behavior shown by the adult in any given situation is thus dependent not only upon the specific stimulus which brings about the response, but also upon his own past experience.

Individual Differences in Adaptation

Emotional responses develop like any habit, and the particular emotion manifested to any stimulus is the result of an habitual method of reaction, determined by past training in meeting similar situations. Two individuals will react differently to the same stimulus from the emotional standpoint. One may show anger, another fear, because this is the method of adjustment he has developed in meeting a particular type of situation. Let us take the example of the reactions of two individuals to the reading of a mystery story. One person may throw the book down after he has finished, calling it "very interesting" or "improbable"; the other may be quite frightened and before he goes to bed will find out whether the doors and windows are locked. The first individual has shown very little emotional reaction to the book, but the other has displayed a distinct fear response. The analysis of their attitudes and behavior gives us a clue to the difference between the two individuals. The one who showed no emotional response disbelieves in and scoffs at the events related in the book. The other, who showed fear, actually has been taking part in the story and reacting bodily to the situations set forth therein. He may say he does not believe the story, but usually will admit that he has given some credence to the events about which he has read. His emotional response is his method of reaction to the book.

Studies of psychopathic individuals give further evidence of the function of emotions as reactions of adaptation to specific stimuli. The absence of emotional response in some types of mentally abnormal individuals is often attributed to deterioration in emotional processes. A so-called emotionally deteriorated individual fails to respond to many stimuli which previously were adequate to produce reactions of emotion; neither pain nor harsh words are effective. But it is not because his capacity for emotional reactions has deteriorated that he no longer responds; it is because he has withdrawn from the social environment in which the original stimuli were effective, and hence because of changes in the type of response which he utilizes in his adjustment to his environment. Their reaction to other types of stimulation is proof that these patients actually do not deteriorate emotionally. The individual who has grandiose ideas of wealth may be immune to situations which produce an emotional response in normal people, but he reacts immediately to any situation involving the notion of his fabulous wealth.

The methods of reeducation and rehabilitation of the insane show clearly that their failure to respond emotionally is due not to inability but to the fact that they respond only to certain types of stimulation. Their behavior is due, furthermore, to the particular method they assume in adjusting to their social situation. The depressed individual most often is obsessed by self-accusatory ideas in which he fears definite consequences. His bodily reaction to his imaginary ideas gives a clue to his emotional response. The elated individual is active and talkative, the depressed patient is more often quiet and reticent. The changes which come about in their emotional responses result directly from their methods of adjustment to the social situation which has produced their behavior.

INFLUENCE OF EARLY EMOTIONAL RESPONSES UPON PERSONALITY

The first two years of life are often said to constitute the important period during which the personality is formed. Without doubt the character of the emotional responses first shown is one of the greatest factors in the determination of traits which develop later, for personality is particularly influenced by the type of emotional response which an individual typically assumes.

The influence of early emotional responses upon personality can be seen even in the young infant. In the hospital nursery at least two types of infant can be distinguished easily—the quiet child who cries rarely except at feeding periods, who is not irritable and who demands little attention from the nurse, and the child who begins to cry long before the feeding period, who is extremely restless and demands considerable attention. In many cases it is found that the former type does not have a private nurse and, therefore, is handled very little except for feeding, clothing and bathing, and is allowed to cry until it becomes quiet. The latter usually has more attention, is picked up frequently to be taken into the mother's room to be shown to visitors, and is rarely allowed to cry very long without being soothed by patting or stroking. There is thus a direct relation between the amount of handling an infant receives and the type of emotional response it develops. Moreover, infants with a private nurse differ among themselves in that the more attention they receive the more irritable and emotionally unstable they are. Student nurses often classify "private" infants as "bad" and "service" infants as "good," although they are inclined to attribute the fidgety, irritable condition of the "bad" infant to some physical condition, such as a disturbance of the intestinal tract. Emotional responses which thus develop within the first week of life are quickly fixed to persist throughout infancy and childhood, arising not only when the original stimuli which first brought them out recur, but also as habitual responses to various other situations.

Studies of young children also indicate the importance of the emotional responses in the determination of personality. Marked characteristic differences can be noted in children as young as two years. One child reacts with a tantrum when it is frustrated, another withdraws from the situation. One is generally aggressive in all his behavior, another cries and seeks help when confronted with a problem. As these various methods of response continue to appear and become habitual, they characterize the personality to a great extent.

Our estimates of most of the personality traits which we ascribe to an individual are based upon the character of his emotional responses. We have already seen that their different reactions to the same story gave us a clue to the personalities of the two individuals who read it. Calmness, irritability, egocentricity, paranoia, shyness, aggressiveness, are all characteristic reactions arising from complex emotional responses built up by experience. An adult may be maladjusted because he has developed an egocentric reaction which prevents him from understanding his own emotional behavior. He may, for example, be the sort of person who has little knowledge of a subject but will discuss it as though he were well versed in it and become quite aggressive if challenged. This type of person is as common among the intellectually superior as among the intellectually inferior. He has developed a characteristic emotional reaction, probably when quite young, which is expressed in almost every situation in which he finds himself.

ORIGIN OF EMOTIONAL DISTURBANCES IN CHILDREN AND ADULTS

An analysis of abnormal disturbances indicates that they also develop as attempts at adaptation. It is popularly believed that "nervousness" and some of the insanities arise because of certain emotional disorders around which further symptoms are built up. But in view of recent studies of the behavior difficulties of children whose abnormalities are not yet well developed and whose condition is not complicated by the many social factors influencing the adult, the attitude toward the role of the emotions in these disorders has changed. These cases show that the primary disturbance is some conflict, of which the emotional upset is a secondary result due to the change necessary in the adjustment of the individual to the conditions which have produced the difficulty. Most marked abnormalities of behavior develop as a result of conflicts which the individual is unable to solve in a satisfactory way, and which he accordingly meets in an unusual manner which marks him as abnormal. One who has aspired to wealth but has encountered many financial difficulties may develop serious conflicts because of the incompatibility between his aims and his achievements. His solution may take the form of ideas in which he believes himself the possessor of a great fortune. The emotional disturbance follows; he becomes elated, excitable and very happy. This disturbed emotional behavior is the method he assumes in responding to the situation which he believes to exist.

Studies of the development of hallucinations show that emotional disorders often follow long after the appearance of unusual behavior. The following history of a boy of ten illustrates the secondary development of an emotional disturbance as an attempt to adjust to hallucinatory experiences, which in turn were the result of conflicts in the environment. The boy was a masturbator and had been beaten severely for it. He also had been told that he would die or go insane if he continued this practice. He developed many fears, particularly fear of the dark, and said he heard voices threatening to kill him. He was very restless at night, and about once a week awakened his mother to tell her that he heard voices calling to him from the hallway. Physically, he was quite well, and his intelligence was about average. He related his hallucinatory experiences in a quiet, placid manner. He stated that he did not fear the voices except at the time of hearing them. He did not know how he happened to hear them, since he could find no one near him, but he was sure they were real. After hearing a particularly large number of voices he would run away from home for a day or two. Usually he went away by himself and wandered around the streets in what was apparently a state of confusion. He first heard sounds which he thought were made by tramps in the alley; a few weeks later he recognized definite voices, heard people, apparently in the alley, shouting to him, "If you don't do that, I'll kill you," and "Get out or I'll kill you." Finally his teacher began to complain of his attacks of violent trembling, loss of self-control and inability to sustain attention. These attacks occurred every day or two and were usually brought on by some slight annoyance.

An analysis of this emotional disturbance showed that it started long after the development of the boy's conflicts and hallucinatory experiences, and that it then occurred characteristically at the time when he experienced the persecutory hallucinations. His unusual emotional outburst was an attempt to adjust to the imaginary persecutions. It is significant also that these unusual emotional responses did not occur until he became certain that the hallucinations were real. When he first began experiencing them he did not respond emotionally, and in telling about the voices, he was quite calm. In other words, the disturbance of his emotional stability developed as a result of his effort to adjust to his particular difficulties.

TREATMENT OF EMOTIONAL DISTURBANCES

We have seen from the experiments described in Chapter V that attempts to name an emotion according to outward characteristics of behavior are often futile without an understanding of the significance of particular adaptive reactions. Thus treatment of behavior disorders based upon their outward manifestations is usually of little value without an analysis of the attempt at adaptation which the behavior shows. Treatment of any emotional disturbance must be directed toward the cause, that is, the specific situation to which the individual is attempting to adjust. If attention is directed to the behavior only, the usual result is an inhibition of that behavior, without a change in the underlying conditions which have produced it. It is possible, in such cases, to so alter the environment that the individual finds emotional responses of no use. He must then substitute another type of response for the one which does not serve him well.

If a child's temper tantrum, for example, is treated only by suppression, little can be done to change the personality of the child. However, if the situation which allows for the tantrum is corrected by training the child to be self-reliant but not domineering, good results usually follow within a short time. An anger tantrum in most cases is directed toward gaining some object otherwise not easily obtained. It is usually an efficacious means of getting one's own way. Studies of children show clearly that this behavior develops by trial and error until finally it adjusts them to a situation in which they wish to dominate. The following case is an example of the rôle of anger in adaptation, and the method by which another type of reaction is substituted when it does not serve its purpose:

Nancy, two years and eight months of age, displayed anger tantrums for some time. Usually these occurred when there were visitors in the home, and many times scenes took place which caused the mother great embarrassment. Her method of handling the situation was to punish the child physically or withhold some of her privileges. On two occasions when the child was to be left at the nursery school, she threw herself on the ground and kicked and screamed until her mother picked her up, made promises and stayed longer with her. On the next occurrence of this incident, the function of Nancy's anger was clearly illustrated. A teacher instructed the mother to leave, and no one in the nursery paid any attention to the child. After a few minutes of kicking and screaming she looked around and apparently saw no one looking at her; she got up, went over to one of the teachers and asked to be allowed to play with the other children. In this case the anger tantrum was quickly stopped when nothing was gained by its continuance.

An anger tantrum is, however, seldom an attempt to gain a goal by deliberately becoming emotionally upset, because the child usually does not reason about his behavior. He simply continues to react with an emotional response that has served him on previous occasions. The fact that behavior is unacceptable socially does not prevent it from being an adaptation.

The treatment of emotional disorders and upsets in children, then, must be constructive. One should attempt neither to quiet them nor to stimulate them, but to find out to what they are trying to adjust by their emotional behavior—whether it be to get attention, to dominate someone, or to obtain certain objects. Children are often regarded as mentally retarded because they are unable to get along with others or unable to learn as well as others, but often the defect is not in the intelligence but due to some emotional disturbance that influences the child's application to school work. By changing the environment and adjusting the child's attitudes and those of the people around him the emotional disturbances, which are secondary to other factors, should disappear.

The child who believes himself abused and dominated by others may develop a disturbance in which he becomes restless and irritable and has anger tantrums. Very little can be done in reestablishing such a child if an attempt is made to treat the emotional disturbance only; his attitudes towards others must be changed and he must be given an understanding of the reasons for his reactions. When he finds it to his advantage to adjust in a different manner to other individuals his emotional disturbance soon disappears.

Aid given by Insight of the Individual into the Stimulating Circumstances

That emotional behavior is determined by the method of reaction utilized in adjusting to a particular situation is also shown by the improvement in emotional stability which occurs when a mode of response is changed for the better. Such reestablishment of emotional stability is greatly aided if the individual can be given insight into his own situation. The child who shows emotional outbursts improves when he understands the reasons for his behavior and its possible consequences. The child whose behavior is described as abnormal can become well adjusted after the origin of his disturbances is pointed out to him and he is shown that his peculiar behavior is the result of conflicts which developed because of his difficulties. Similar changes also result in the emotional responses of neurotic individuals after they recognize that their unusual behavior is due to conflicts which can be solved.

That the emotional responses of the individual are affected by his lack of insight into his own behavior is evident in children suffering from the after-effects of encephalitis (sleeping sickness). Many of these children show behavior which apparently is highly emotional, consisting of irritability, quarrelsomeness, and outbursts of temper. They display sudden periods of apparent anger during which they become destructive or strike others without cause. Almost invariably they are unable to account for their sudden outbursts of temper. Their statements show that they feel no anger, and many of them cannot understand why the parents or teacher describe them as showing it. After a number of months of this type of behavior entirely different attitudes develop. They begin to recognize their emotional reactions as anger and readily admit that they get very angry at the least annoyance. This change in attitude shows that emotional responses develop during the attempted adjustment to already existing behavior. These children have been influenced by others to believe

that their behavior denotes anger, although they
have no understanding of and certainly do not
give a name to their outbursts. They finally call
these disturbances anger and develop an anger response in connection with them.

Chapter VII

THE DEVELOPMENT OF PERSONALITY

A DEFINITION OF PERSONALITY

PERSONALITY is the characteristic behavior of an individual. This characteristic behavior is evident throughout his daily activities, but is especially noticeable in his manner of meeting new situations. We may characterize one person by his perseverance, another by his egocentricity or by his shyness. A certain reaction pattern, although never rigid, nevertheless dominates the activities of every individual to the extent that he manifests definite characteristics in much of his behavior.

The methods used by the individual in adjusting to his environment determine his personality in large part. The good-natured, contented person accepts his position in life and has no major conflicts; the irritable, nervous person, on the other hand, has developed conflicts as a result of some incompatibility between his situation (actual or imagined) and his wishes. The reactions which follow these conditions are transferred to many situations other than the original one which caused the difficulty, and this transfer of a reaction in one situation to many others is the basis of the development of a dominant type of response which characterizes the individual. Such a transfer may begin very early in life and can be observed readily even in infants below ten days of age. They often become unusually irritable at feeding time, for example; soon after the development of this characteristic, they behave in a similar way when being bathed or dressed. Infants very soon begin to develop overt behavior which becomes distinctive for them.

The individual's general method of adjustment to his environment, although it largely determines his personality, is never static but constantly undergoes change. Different traits predominate under different conditions; when the social situation which forms the basis of particular characteristics changes, the personality also changes. These changes can be seen in all individuals. In order to achieve a satisfactory adjustment, any modification of the environment must necessarily produce a change in the character of the responses made to it. Both the growing child and the adult are constantly confronted by new conditions, by problems which must be solved, and old methods of reaction give way to new. If the personality of an adult is not modified by the solution of particular difficulties, this is because he has developed a definite pattern of response which is so habitual that it is not readily altered.

EARLY CHARACTERISTICS OF PERSONALITY

The early characteristics of personality are not sufficiently clearly defined or dominant to make possible extensive differentiation between infants. During the first few weeks of life, the characteristics a child shows are necessarily limited because of his incomplete physical growth and undeveloped emotional responses, and the restrictions of a uniform environment. Yet, in spite of these limitations young infants do show individual characteristics of behavior, and the attendants in a nursery recognize differences in the responses of various children to feeding, bathing and other care. These characteristics develop as adaptive reactions to particular conditions, and become fairly habitual quite early.

Infants can sometimes be differentiated from each other by their reaction to food. Most infants usually sleep or rest until a short time before the feeding period, but some become extremely irritable long before feeding time and cry almost continuously. The only reason for such behavior, other than the physical condition of hunger, is that the child has developed an exaggerated reaction toward the feeding period. He has learned to respond to the onset of hunger by irritability and crying because in his past experience crying before the feeding period was followed by certain sensory consequences. The nurse may have picked him up or soothed him in some other way when he began to cry, and thus he developed a habit of crying in order to reinstate an agreeable sensory situation.

A child may be very sensitive to stimuli which in most infants do not result in any definite response. This is due to a lowering of the threshold of excitability to these stimuli either by repeated stimulation or by some conditioning process whereby the infant makes use of the response aroused by one type of stimulus in many other situations. For instance, if he has become irritable when his clothing is changed, he may react in a similar way to any of the other forms of stimulation which occur in the usual nursery routine.

As the child begins to adjust to more persons and circumstances his general method of response becomes more and more typical. By the age of two, marked differences are evident in the types of behavior to which children resort most consistently: one is jealous or aggressive when attention is paid to another child; one runs away from a difficult situation; one is forward and bold, another shy; one tends to bully other children, another cries and seeks help when they interfere with him.

Many of the personality reactions of young children are strikingly similar to those of the adult. In general the child differs from the adult in not inhibiting his overt responses as the latter has learned to do. Because of his undeveloped intelligence the child does not understand the consequences of his reactions, but responds to every situation in an attempt to reach an immediate goal. In this respect the difference between the child and the adult is comparable to that between animal and man. The animal responds to the immediate situation but man is able to deliberate and weigh the possible consequences of his behavior. The young child has not learned to differentiate between various environmental conditions. He reacts in his characteristic manner whether he is at home, on the playground with a group of children, or with adults. As his experience in social situations increases, his manner of reaction changes and his personality characteristics are increasingly modified by the new conditions he meets.

Development of Conflicts

Although it is often said that conflicts are peculiar to the youth or adult, and that they affect the child but slightly, numerous facts show that they play an important rôle in early childhood and have far-reaching effects upon personality. The growing child necessarily must adjust continually to new conditions and, therefore, is constantly confronted with problems. Most people regard the problems of children with less concern than those of the adult, possibly because of the latter's immediate economic and social importance. Since the child lives in a restricted and protected environment, his conflicts are not always obvious. An analysis of children's characteristics shows, however, that many of them develop as attempts to adjust to some conflict. When an adult becomes "temperamental" he is likely to lose his job or get into other difficulties, but a child who creates a disturbance is reprimanded or his behavior is attributed to poor training, and nothing further is done about it. Some of his conflicts may be solved early in life, but many continue indefinitely. Some of the unsolved conflicts are of minor importance and cause no difficulties, but others that involve a major issue often have serious effects.

Conflicts arise because of discrepancies between existing conditions and the individual's demands. In the lives of most children surprisingly many situations occur which lead to serious difficulties later on. As soon as the child is able to differentiate himself from others socially and to understand the significance of his reactions, he begins to face problems. A shift from his circumscribed environment and personal dependence to a wider social sphere favors the development of conflicts because he lacks understanding of the changed conditions. The two-year-old who has always had his own way in his home is suddenly confronted, in the nursery school, with a situation in which he must share his possessions with others. He expects his home behavior to be successful elsewhere and is unhappy when he discovers that outsiders resist and resent his assertive tendencies. When a child is acquainted gradually with individuals other than his own family and at the same time is taught that he must coöperate with others, such conflicts do not arise.

Effects of Authority

If the child's spontaneity is restricted by too much authority, conflicts develop when he realizes that he has been unfairly treated. Difficulties because of subjection to severe authority arise very early in the lives of many children. As soon as they begin to walk and come in contact with objects, authority begins to be asserted. For the first time they are given inhibitory commands, and begin to hear numerous "don'ts"—don't break this, don't play there, don't eat so fast, don't get dirty. It is not surprising that the child soon rebels against his parents' attempts to direct him. Authoritative commands are dangerous, and often do not work at all.

The following case of a boy who at four years began to stutter illustrates clearly the effect of too authoritative an attitude on the part of a parent. The boy's father, believing in old-fashioned strictness, had always treated him harshly. No deleterious effects of this training were observed until the child was about four years of age, when he developed numerous fears for which he could give no explanation. Shortly after, he began to stutter. He was well developed physically, and superior in intelligence. Although his ability in all kinds of mechanical tasks was very good, he underestimated himself. When asked to show his skill on several pieces of apparatus, he immediately said he couldn't do anything with them, but when urged, he performed very well. He was shy and retiring in all new situations, as though waiting to see what would happen. He said he was always afraid of doing things because he did not know how his father would like it. He said that sometimes he was afraid of his father, and that sometimes his father locked him in the cellar or attic. He said God and his father were both observing his behavior; God could see everywhere; God would punish him if he were bad.

As a result of his fear of his father he hated him, and at the same time he wanted to be like him. Conflicts developed which very soon resulted in definite difficulties. Punishment had made a coward of the child. Fear of his father was transferred to other situations; he was afraid of the boys in his neighborhood, although many of them were weaker than he; he feared sleeping alone, feared going into a dark room lest something should "get" him, would not go into the cellar or attic alone, and so on.

In compensation he developed a boastful attitude; he described other boys as afraid to fight with him because they knew he would win, and spoke of his cruelty to others. Actually, the friends he chose did not like to fight, and were younger and smaller than he. His phantasies were entirely concerned with fighting. At these times he thought of his father, and of boys he would like to beat.

Religious training is very often a factor in the development of fears. The four-year-old is taught to think of God as some one who watches over him, who can see everywhere and keeps him from being "bad." As a result of attitudes which religious training produces, fear of being observed doing wrong may develop. A child should never be taught that anything he does is "bad." Uncertainty about one's behavior often leads to confusion and makes it necessary to have help in reaching every decision. Apprehension is the basis of many neurotic characteristics. Because of it an individual undervalues his own abilities, approaches situations with temerity, and concerns himself constantly with what others think of him.

The Influence of Training

Every dominant characteristic of personality is influenced by training. The responses of all newborn infants are very similar, and in a well managed nursery where they are fed, handled and treated generally in a uniform fashion it is often difficult to differentiate between them. Whatever differences exist probably are due to the physical condition of the child. The differences in personality which may be observed within a few weeks, however, can be traced in most cases to differences in training, that is, in the type of conditions to which the infant must adjust and the manner in which they occur. Sudden picking up on repeated occasions will result in habits which are not shown by a child who is handled carefully. One can always observe differences in infants who are managed differently by their nurses. Excessive handling and excitation are factors in developing an irritable, aggressive personality instead of a stable even-tempered one. The degree of irritability or assertiveness or any other trait is determined almost directly by the treatment of the child.

Training of infants connotes much broader terms than training for skill or for a vocation. Nevertheless, the methods by which personality is developed are quite similar to those by which any habit is formed. The effect of the method of training upon the formation of personality is much greater during the first years of life than later, because the young child has not yet developed many definite characteristics, and because he is much more flexible than an older child who may have formed habits which must be eliminated before new ones can develop. Although the activities of the newborn infant are largely random, he begins to develop patterns of response in his very first attempts to adjust to his environment, and what he becomes depends largely upon the nature of that environment.

Personality characteristics are habitual responses which become more and more permanent as they are repeated. A new form of behavior becomes fixated very quickly, unless means are taken to suppress it soon after its appearance. Some writers maintain that the personality of a child develops definitely at about two years of age; others believe this occurs at one year, still others at three years. It perhaps is more accurate to say that the personality is determined as soon as a general type of reaction is repeated sufficiently to become fixated. Some personality traits certainly develop as early as the first or second week of life.

Specific personality characteristics depend upon the type of adaptive responses which the individual makes use of. One child learns that a temper tantrum brings attention or satisfaction of his wishes. Another attains the same results by sulking or crying if these particular methods have been successful in the past. In each case the method which attains the goal is soon established. Then behavior which recurs frequently is soon transferred to situations other than those which originally aroused it, and continues as a personality characteristic. As in the case of the nursery-school child, many of the older child's problems are the result of a transfer to the school of a behavior pattern developed in response to brothers and sisters in the home. Examples of the development of antisocial behavior as the result of teasing or bullying by older children in the home are numerous. Under these conditions a child may develop many fears and attempt to compensate for them by assuming a domineering attitude toward his playmates. These children become troublesome because they continually interfere with the activities of other children and constantly seek attention by disturbing methods. They usually are unhappy unless they can lead and they expect others to follow their directions. If they are not retrained, emotional disturbances of a serious nature often result, because their difficulties increase as they come in contact with an increasingly complex social environment.

The results of the early training a child receives manifest themselves as soon as he begins to make social adaptations, and can be observed in children much younger than those of school age. The following example illustrates the effect of early experience and the rapidity with which maladjustment occurs as a result of faulty home training:

Paul, a boy less than three years of age, became difficult to manage almost as soon as he entered the nursery school. He refused to make friends with any of the children there, preferring to play by himself. He constantly interfered with the activities of others, took their toys from them and apparently enjoyed breaking up their games. He became sulky when attention was called to his destructive behavior and proceeded with it as soon as the teachers left him. The reason for this behavior became apparent when the home situation was investigated. The parents had a great deal of difficulty with Paul whenever he and his older brother were together. This other boy, nine years of age, constantly teased Paul by taking away his toys. He appeared to be delighted with the temper tantrums of the three-year-old and seemed never to tire of interfering with his activities. Paul's antagonism to this grew and was transferred to situations involving other children. Unable to compete with his bigger brother, he took the opportunity to interfere with children his own age.

Unless an effort is made to suppress antisocial habits and to substitute for them coöperative tendencies, these detrimental personality characteristics become firmly fixed. The popular belief that an individual's personality is determined at five or six years of age does not tell the whole story. Many traits are established much earlier, and changes for the better often are difficult to effect because these traits have become habitual. Undesirable characteristics can usually be changed, however, if the environment is altered and the child is thus given an opportunity to change his methods of adjustment. Numerous examples of how social habits may be substituted for antisocial ones, bringing about an almost complete change of personality, may be found in any group of young children.

Shirley, for example, a girl somewhat over two years of age, entered nursery school and was recognized immediately as a shy, retiring and unfriendly child. Feeding was also a problem with her, as she refused to eat the food served. She required a great deal of urging before she would take part in the activities of the other children, and so was placed in a group of about twenty who were encouraged to make friends with her. Within a short time she changed almost completely. She began to show an interest in games and in other group activities, began making numerous friends and instead of playing by herself preferred to be with other children. She changed from a rather sullen follower to a cheerful leader who, however, was never domineering. In this case the causes of the original behavior were an overprotective mother and a lack of social contacts. She had learned to be entirely dependent upon her mother and was unable at first to show any initiative or to take part in group activities.

Flexibility of personality responses is reached only after a long learning process which begins early in childhood and continues indefinitely. If a child is not given the opportunity at an early age to learn to react to various social situations he gets into difficulty as soon as he must adjust to a group wider than that in the home. Some children are so protected that they have little chance for contact with many individuals in varied circumstances. The child who has not been allowed to play freely with other children until he is four or five years of age usually finds this difficult when the time arrives for him to begin to cooperate with a group. Teachers in the lower grades frequently must solve the problems of such children.

The kindergarten, in addition to teaching every child the routine of concentrated application not learned during the years of independent play, helps to bridge the gap between the restricted life of the home and the group life of the school. The recent nursery school movement was begun in recognition of the value of social adaptation to children even younger than the kindergarten age. Personality changes take place rapidly when the child is placed in a wider social environment than that of his home, and is given an opportunity to respond to a large number of children and adults and to various situations in which coöperation is essential.

THE RELATION OF SENSORI-MOTOR RESPONSES AND INTELLIGENCE TO PERSONALITY

The way in which the child responds to various sensory situations is one of the important elements in the development of his personality. If the sensori-motor responses are sluggish, for instance, the personality may be characterized by a sluggish response under most conditions, and if they are quick, the individual is likely to be of an active, impulsive type. Infants one month old show differences in the manner in which they react to various stimuli. The character of the reflex responses to touch and pain, for example, varies in different infants and influences the type of reaction and the habits which develop later on. One may react suddenly, another very slowly; one is very sensitive to pain or handling, another scarcely responds. We have seen that excessive handling and excitation are factors in the development of an irritable, aggressive personality and that training influences every dominant characteristic of personality. As all newborn infants are very insensitive to stimulation, differences that arise must be mainly the result of experience which influences the characteristic responses of the child.

Insensitivity to pain or temperature, for example, which infants sometimes show, has a definite relation to personality characteristics. Children described as tractable and quiet are often found to have sluggish responses. A child who shows the reactivity which accompanies well developed sensori-motor responses, on the other hand, is usually described by attendants as irritable and difficult. If a child responds explosively to pain he is not easily handled and is said to adjust poorly to his environment; but if he is sluggish he is described as good. The school child who is not irritable in school situations is considered well-adjusted, but one who is over-active and responds suddenly and with emotion is said to be unadjusted. In the same way one finds that adults who are sluggish in their sensori-motor responses are considered to be well-adjusted to their environment, but those who have a high degree of activity and are quick in all their reactions usually are suspected of being somewhat unstable.

A child who is highly sensitive to stimulation and whose reactions are quick often has a greater versatility of interests than one who reacts slowly and methodically, although the latter may have excellent learning ability and a good understanding of particular problems. Often the versatile, sensitive child is unstable physically and has a high rate of metabolism. He is less able to concentrate for long periods of time than the more stolid, well-nourished and less responsive child because his quick reactions to stimulation detract from his performance of any particular task.

The amount of stimulation which a young child receives influences the spontaneity he shows toward his surroundings—a characteristic of personality —and the rate and character of his growth in intelligence, for the two are related. Within the average range, however, the degree of variation in intelligence between one individual and another does not greatly influence the personality. A child with an intelligence quotient of 90 may be

quite different from one with a slightly higher
quotient, but the difference can not reasonably be
due to intelligence alone. Where large variations
from the average exist, however, intelligence does
influence personality because it partly determines
the specific characteristics finally established.
Adequate intelligence allows a person to understand his environment and the significance of his
reactions, making it possible for him to change
characteristics which would bring about maladjustment. The detrimental personality traits
which feeble-minded children often display as a
result of limited comprehension of their own behavior are not readily changed even when the
environment is altered, because these children do
not understand the significance and consequences
of their acts.

The Factor of Physical Condition in Personality

Physical condition often influences the personality by determining the kind of responses the individual is able to make. The excessively large
person whose rate of metabolism is low reacts
sluggishly, and as a result is usually stable and
even-tempered. On the other hand, a person with
a high metabolic rate is likely to have a high degree of sensitivity and quick and exaggerated re-

actions, so that he is very responsive to all sorts of conditions.

Changes in personality are often seen in disease. In hyperthyroidism, for example, where there is an excessive secretion of the thyroid gland, the metabolic rate is increased, there is a loss of weight, a coarse tremor of the hands, and other physical symptoms. Coincident with the development of the disease, changes in personality take place. A calm, well-controlled individual becomes cross, irritable and quarrelsome. Various signs of nervousness appear, such as emotional instability, sleeplessness, and apprehensiveness. The disappearance of these signs when a normal physical condition is reëstablished, following treatment, clearly illustrates the relation of various characteristics of personality to the physical condition.

Changes in personality often occur because of an attempt to compensate for some physical defect. If the defect is striking, it may have a significant effect upon behavior. Usually it is not the actual physical condition that modifies the reactions of these individuals, however, but it is their emotional response to the physical condition that influences the type of attitudes they develop regarding their defects. The sick or crippled child frequently is concerned about his inability to take part in the normal activities of other children. He may become engrossed in himself, shy, antagonistic to friends, or he may attempt to dominate those about him by displays of rage. As a result, these children often are extremely difficult to manage. The person who is physically abnormal compares himself with others until he is forced to make some compensation for his defect. He either develops attitudes of inferiority, reticence and shyness, which frequently lead to serious maladjustment, or he may seek various means of making himself attractive and admired, as by being unusually careful about his personal appearance, or by striving for perfection in some game of skill.

EMOTIONAL RESPONSES AND PERSONALITY

The most important influence determining the personality of the child who is normal physically and mentally is his characteristic type of emotional response. Even where the mental and physical development are not normal this is true to a great extent. A defective child often has excessive emotional disturbances because he is unable to adjust to ordinary situations quickly. A child who has particular difficulty in doing his school work very often becomes unstable because the demands made upon him are too great for his capacity; indeed, many of the problems which teachers experience with school children illustrate the effects which poor ability has upon the emotions. Even fancied physical or mental defects, again, may result in emotional responses which become typical for the individual. When fear predominates, shyness and a tendency to retire from new situations are characteristic; when anger results from the frequent thwarting of progress, stubbornness and aggressiveness are characteristic.

Differences in the personalities of young children are for the most part due to the differences in their characteristic emotional responses. The typical reaction to a difficult situation may be anger, or it may be fear with retreat. A child may be assertive and wish to dominate those about him and have anger tantrums when suppressed, or he may be docile and accept guidance readily. Typical emotional responses develop early in childhood and are transferred to the more complex situations confronting the youth and adult. The appearance of anger tantrums in a child is nearly always preceded by explosive emotional reactions during infancy. The sudden, continued emotional reaction of an infant to a situation which ordinarily calls out very little emotional response is a characteristic quite similar to the anger tantrum of the older child. The egocentric behavior of some adults is similarly related to the typical emotional reactions they showed earlier in life.

The excitable type of individual responds quickly emotionally and shows frequent changes of emotion. An excitable child easily becomes sullen, or fearful, or aggressive. The excitable person is often told to consider a situation before reacting to it, the familiar advice "count ten before you act" referring to the need for control of emotional behavior. When a person deliberates about his procedure he will not react in an extreme fashion emotionally, which indicates that an emotional response is one method of adjusting to a situation but other better methods may be substituted. The phlegmatic individual's emotional responses are slow and without vacillation. The difference between the excitable and the phlegmatic person is similar to the difference between individuals with a quick and a slow reaction time. Each has a definite method of reaction by which he is characterized.

Anger Tantrums and Other Disorders

As we have seen, various types of detrimental emotional response which influence the make-up of a personality are ordinarily modified when the individual gains insight into the reasons for his behavior and recognizes its social significance. A child quickly ceases to have anger tantrums when he realizes that they do not attain results. Often a child is very stable emotionally and has few, if any, objectionable social responses while in the nursery school, but at home behaves quite differently, having frequent anger tantrums. The reason for this difference is that the child realizes, even though to a slight extent, the significance of his emotional responses and that an anger tantrum will not attain results in the school but does in the home. We have already seen that the treatment of emotional upsets depends upon a knowledge of the reasons for the response and the discovery of the goal sought; with these two factors established they can be treated with much less difficulty than is usual in the home.

Parents sometimes complain that one child in the family teases another, and that no measures taken to stop it are successful. What such a child really wants is attention from his parents, although he may not get the kind of notice he prefers. Teasing usually is quickly stopped when no one pays attention to it.

All of the personality characteristics of the neurotic, the insane, or the dissociated personality result from emotional disturbances. Thus the paranoid individual who believes that others are against him has developed the attitude that his importance is not understood, and as a justification has begun to consider his friends and acquaintances as enemies. Whenever he thinks of himself as a failure, he explains his difficulties to himself by assuming that others are responsible for his misfortunes. Similarly other abnormal personality traits are due to the development of emotions which arise because of conflict between opposing motives, and finally produce some dominant characteristic which results in maladjustment. When an emotional response becomes sufficiently intense, compensatory behavior develops. Thus egocentricity is a compensatory reaction to a real or fancied inferiority from which an individual attempts to escape by elevating his own importance and decreasing that of others.

The influence of the emotional responses upon the personality becomes less evident as the emotions change with experience. Resentment, for instance, which nearly always is demonstrated as an aggressive type of activity in a young child may later show itself in a less overt manner and be expressed in some planned form of revenge. The other emotional responses also are gradually inhibited; the older the child the less obvious are his emotional reactions, because as he grows older and learns that standards of good manners and of bravery do not allow for excessive emotional expression, he becomes better and better able to direct and control them. The extent to which he can do this again distinctly constitutes a characteristic of his personality.

Chapter VIII

PERSONALITY AND SOCIAL BEHAVIOR

PERSONALITY TYPES

PERSONALITIES are often classified into distinct types on the basis of one of the following assumptions: first, that individuals are born with a predisposition to develop a particular type of personality, and secondly, that personality characteristics have a definite pattern that is not easily changed. But while it is convenient at times to classify personality into distinct groups, any classification is arbitrary and cannot be made on the supposition that the behavior of any group of individuals is fixed and static. Indeed, these assumptions must be denied in view of recent evidence. We have seen that the responses utilized in adapting to the environment are learned through experience, developing out of the primary aimless reactions of the infant. Personality traits develop in a similar manner, as methods of adjustment to a given environment, and every normal person modifies his characteristics to meet the demands of his surroundings.

The first two or three years of a child's life are exceedingly important in determining his personality, for it is during this period that the definite adaptive reactions to the environment which form the basis of particular traits become generalized processes of adjustment. The young child behaves in the school as he does in the home; as his reactions become more habitual they are utilized in other social situations and he is soon characterized by certain dominant traits. No personality trait is stable and fixed, however, but all are modified as changes in the environment necessitate alteration in behavior.

A child is often shy with adults but forward and bold with children his own age. Adults show similar variations in behavior. They are rarely shy with those who do not differ greatly from them, but are likely to be reticent with people supposedly superior to them intellectually and whose interests are different from their own. It is true that many individuals avoid social situations and are characterized by this trait. The pattern of their personality is not due to any hereditary predisposition, however, but to the particular method of response they have adopted.

Certain physical characteristics, intellectual capacities and environmental conditions certainly do exist which favor specific personality traits. Differences in personality which apparently result from the physical make-up have led some authors to theorize about constitutional personality types. Thus they classify personalities into the athletic and other types on the assumption that personality traits are inherently determined by structure. One can readily see, however, that these types are not due to innate predispositions, but to the physical, metabolic and nutritional condition, and to sensitivity and speed of reactivity.

We have already discussed the factor of physical condition and its effects upon personality. Even very young infants give evidence of this effect. A sick child is more irritable than a healthy one. An undernourished child cries more often, is likely to react more quickly and decisively than the well-nourished child, and responds to more stimuli that ordinarily are ineffective. Quick and decisive reactions are usually valuable, but when over-emphasized they may become detrimental. Apparently a malnourished condition increases excitability and speed of reaction. (Whether this is due to malnourishment itself, or to the resulting production of toxins, is not known.) When a child of this type is treated for his physical condition and improves, many of his personality characteristics, which otherwise may become habitual, change considerably. Because personality traits develop early in life and sometimes continue essentially unchanged we cannot conclude that personality is inherently predetermined.

The normal, well-adjusted person rarely has traits which dominate his conduct entirely. When egocentricity, timidity, aggressiveness, or any other characteristic is so dominant that it can be recognized easily it is the result of an effort to compensate because of some difficulty. Attitudes of inferiority, for example, may give rise to egocentricity that is obvious even to the casual observer. Nevertheless such an individual is able to suppress this trait when it does not adapt him to a situation. The personality remains inflexible and unchanged only in the mentally abnormal who have lost insight into the consequences of their behavior. The following brief accounts illustrate the difference in flexibility of personality in a normal and an abnormal person.

A certain adult whose egocentricity can be traced to the fact of his having been laughed at during his youth because of his physical make-up often attempts to dominate his associates, his point of view is inflexible, and he is described as a "bully." But when he meets someone with prestige or finds himself in a situation where he must calculate his reactions carefully, his characteristics change immediately; he becomes coöperative and ingratiating, and expresses his willingness to follow directions and to profit by training.

Another individual of about the same age, who has been in a sanitarium on several occasions, differs very little during periods of normality from the man just described. But during periods of abnormality he is extremely egocentric, and talks incessantly about his good intelligence, his earning capacity, and his power. During these periods he does not allow contradiction, and behaves alike with people who have or have not prestige for him. In other words, he has lost insight into reality and is unable to distinguish between situations which are beneficial and those which are detrimental to him. Because of his inability to change his reactions and his lack of insight into the consequences of his behavior he is characterized as abnormal. He differs from the man first described in the degree to which egocentricity dominates his behavior.

The traits which predominate at any time depend upon the situation to which the individual must adjust. A child observed in a clinic may appear to be very shy or very resistant, but his personality cannot be characterized on this basis alone, because the dominant traits he shows are his reaction to the immediate environment only. In another situation the same child probably shows different characteristics. A child entering a nursery school for the first time is often classified as an "introvert" because he is shy and unable to make friends. Within three or four days, however, as he learns to respond to the new situation, he may become aggressive, domineering and "extroverted," and is then characterized by a different set of traits. The personality of a school child who is reported to be doing poor work and realizes that his teachers are becoming increasingly intolerant of his failures may change considerably. From an affable, sympathetic and obedient child he may become irritable, disobedient, and aggressive; he may begin to annoy other children because he seeks expression in activity which gives him satisfaction; or he may become stubborn and refuse to go to school.

Dissociation

That circumstances determine the traits which characterize a personality is also clearly seen in individuals whose personality is dissociated, that is "split" into independent units. This is observed most often in the mentally abnormal. The following case illustrates the beginning of dissociation. A boy of fourteen complained of nervousness and of something moving in his head and body. He argued with himself about being good or bad, and whether he should fight with other boys. One part of him seemed to say, "be good" and another, "be bad." Soon he saw a person on each side of him, one saying, "be good" and the other, "be bad." His first reaction to these hallucinations was that of anger. He thought the figures were imaginary, but before long they became real to him. One had long hair and was dressed in white—he was God; the other had short hair and was dressed in black—he was the devil. The boy's intelligence was defective and he had been unable to get along in school. He noticed that other boys of his age were advancing more rapidly than he, and he worried about his failures. He was larger than the other boys in his room, and began to quarrel and fight with them. He became a truant and delinquent. His numerous conflicts finally gave rise to a dissociation of his personality as a means of justification for his behavior. On the one hand he was good, and on the other bad—and he attributed his delinquencies and fighting to the person whose voice he heard saying, "be bad."

Every normal individual may be said to possess a number of personalities, since the outstanding characteristics of a personality depend upon the situation to which adjustment is made. As soon as a child is old enough to understand his relation to his environment and begins to gain knowledge of the consequences of his behavior, he modifies his personality according to the conditions he must meet.   Thus a person reacts otherwise in a theater than in church or school.   Every situation arouses a characteristic mode of reaction.   A person in an important social setting for the first time may behave in an inhibited manner because he does not know how he will be received.   He therefore proceeds cautiously and changes his reactions as he gains experience.   Although the normal person may behave very differently in different situations, he understands that the reactions which adjust him to one situation do not adjust him to another, and he is able to change from one to the other easily. The abnormal individual, on the other hand, has lost insight into the difference between his various characteristics and is unable to adapt his reactions to fit specific situations.

Substitution of Traits

Substitution of one trait for another is very common, and any personality type which characterizes an individual at one time may not necessarily do so at other times.   A student frequently changes his taciturn reaction in the classroom to assertiveness when he finds that such a change influences his scholastic record favorably.   Nevertheless, the same individual may continue to be quiet and diffident in other situations where that type of behavior is to his advantage.

An individual is often unaware, however, of the conditions which have produced his characteristics. The youth who longs to be recognized as an artist frequently develops mannerisms which distinguish him from the average person. A boy of seventeen, in the second year of High School and doing poor work, became increasingly argumentative with his teachers, criticized them openly, and refused to do the required work. He also expressed his arrogance at home, where he argued at length about trivial affairs. Although his intelligence was fair, it was scarcely sufficient for him to complete High School successfully, but he explained his failure on the basis of his disinterestedness in the subjects taught and the manner in which they were presented. He admitted that he didn't care to follow the instructions of his teachers and believed their criticisms were aimed at him personally. He said that he wanted to become a novelist and would quit school since he couldn't get adequate training there. He left home and joined a group of pseudo-artists who were trying to gain notoriety as a compensation for their previous failures. Even in this situation, however, he was unable to gain recognition since he brought nothing new into the group. Within six months many people pointed him out as a "peculiar" boy who might be a genius. His hair was long, he wore a large bow tie, trousers different in color and texture from his coat, and carried a cane. In this way he gained recognition and appeared to be an outstanding fellow. He did not realize that he used artificial means to gain attention and that his outstanding characteristics had little social value.

The recognition of the consequences of his behavior is one of the important factors influencing the type of personality which an individual displays. A child of three who is aggressive at home is likely to be aggressive with his playmates and others. He does not appreciate the significance of his behavior and exhibits the same characteristics wherever appropriate stimuli occur. The adult, on the other hand, may be quarrelsome and unpleasant at home but find it disadvantageous to show the same characteristics in his place of employment. The persistently egocentric, aggressive individual does not recognize that he is generally disliked because of these characteristics; his personality changes only when he realizes that they are detrimental to him. Thus we see that the amount of a person's insight into his behavior is one of the most important of the many factors influencing personality type.

NORMALITY AND ABNORMALITY

Many people believe that the normal person never shows any peculiarities or deviations of behavior. Others think of normality as a relative term, that is, that every person is abnormal in some respect. Although we can compare some characteristic of an individual with what we call "the average," this average may not represent what is really typical for the group, for unusual measures often influence the average in one direction or another. The average may thus tell us little about the tendencies of the group as a whole except that its members approach the given value in the characteristic measured.

An average of any random sample of cases only approximates the true average of the entire population, and even if we could measure some characteristic of that population, the average would still be somewhat in error; for it is impossible to measure any characteristic with absolute accuracy because no instruments of measure are perfect and we make errors in using instruments. The average is therefore never a single value but a range of values that includes above and below the arithmetical average an amount of error that has been determined statistically. Thus we should speak of average height or weight not in terms of a single value but of a range of measures which represents the majority of people. For the same reasons we must consider social adjustment in terms of a range of satisfactory adaptability. Behavior especially cannot be judged according to any specific average, but only as it relates to a wide range of activities.

The normal person progresses at the average rate for his age physically and intellectually, and does not come into conflict with his environment. The limitations of normality here implied are determined by the statistical average which includes a range of values representative of most cases. Since there is a range of normality, people necessarily differ from each other in any of their characteristics.

The term abnormal immediately suggests a deviation from the normal, but it is often difficult to distinguish between the two when personality and social adjustment are concerned. In such cases any demarcation is somewhat arbitrary because abnormality increases by imperceptible gradations; it is only when large differences exist that a person can be definitely classified as abnormal.

Personality characteristics of the abnormal frequently differ from the normal mainly in the degree to which they influence behavior. Egocentricity, for example, although common to a great many normal persons, may be so dominant that maladjustment results. This is obvious in some mental diseases, where ideas of persecution result from extreme egocentricity.

Often a person is temporarily maladjusted in a

specific environment, but this does not mean that
he is abnormal. Perhaps the situation is one by
which he is not ordinarily confronted. Continuous maladjustment in a new environment, however, is often a distinguishing feature of abnormality, especially when the individual makes no effort
to improve.

Some situations exist, on the other hand, to
which an abnormal individual makes a good adjustment. The insane, for example, adapt themselves to the routine of the psychopathic hospital.
This in itself does not indicate normality because
the hospital is not representative of the typical environment in which most people live. Normal
social adjustment must be defined in terms of an
environment not created specifically for an individual.

Most of the population of reformatories and
prisons are well adjusted during their imprison-
ment; they follow directions, do productive work,
and do not come into conflict with authority. In
the routine life of the institution they are protected
from unusual situations and are under continual
direction. The amount of restriction in the environment and the degree of supervision of daily
routine must be taken into account in evaluating
a person's ability to react satisfactorily to social
conditions.

THE RÔLE OF PERSONALITY IN SOCIAL BEHAVIOR

We have seen that the young child is likely to exhibit the same characteristics in various situations. As he gains experience, however, he begins to modify his reactions according to the situation. Thus when a child reaches the age of five or six he can be quiet during school hours and does not behave in the same way in a stranger's house as in his own playroom. Satisfactory social adjustment in many instances requires an actual inhibition of characteristics which the child ordinarily manifests. The adult has learned to suppress his emotions; although the presence of an acquaintance may arouse his antagonism, social custom requires that he inhibit this response. Personality characteristics which are inhibited eventually become sufficiently flexible to permit of adaptation in a variety of situations without effort.

A continual change of personality accompanies the improvement in adjustment which occurs as development increases. The usual egocentric "know-it-all" attitude of the High School boy gives way to a more tolerant attitude when he reaches college, and is still further changed when he leaves school entirely to enter competitive social life. This change comes about because of increasing insight into his own and others' behavior and the realization of the necessity for coöperation. A striking similarity is often noted between the egocentric boy and the adult who lacks information. A person who has had little experience or training may be certain and emphatic in his statements, often because of attitudes of inferiority for which he finds it necessary to compensate by garrulousness and assurance.

Personality is indeed the most important factor in the ability to adjust socially. Physical disability may lead to maladjustment, but in such cases the individual usually compensates for his defects by emphasizing some other characteristic. Unless the intelligence status is below the average it also has little influence on social adaptation. In our complex environment the vocational, social and other adjustments which must be made on the basis of intelligence are soon defined for us. While there is some effort to make vocational choice and placement in a less haphazard fashion, and while the individual without technical knowledge usually soon learns to fit into a suitable occupation, many instances exist in which maladjustments occur because of superiority to the environment. A person who is superior to his job may become restless and dissatisfied and develop conflicts which interfere with his work. The effects of such maladjustments are usually expressed in emotional disturbances; and indeed most behavior difficulties, whether due to physical or to intellectual causes, are finally manifested in conflicts characterized by emotional disorganization. The final criterion of any maladjustment which becomes apparent to others is therefore based upon the character of the emotional responses which, as we have seen, are more closely related to the personality than any other factor.

Real or imagined inferiority also frequently results in conflicts, with consequent maladjustment; over-compensation may then follow in the form of an exaggerated belief in physical, intellectual, social or financial ability. Thus the abnormal individual who believes he possesses great wealth is often one who has always been poor, and one who believes himself famous is one who has failed to obtain recognition. The following brief description of two such individuals illustrates the way in which attempts to compensate for environmental difficulties result in personality changes.

A man of thirty-seven, a patient in a sanitarium, was very affable and coöperative, and quite talkative. He boasted of his excellent physical condition and of his financial powers. He maintained that he owned twenty hotels and a hundred thousand houses, and promised those around him large sums of money. His stream of talk always included a discussion of wealth and he managed persistently to turn every conversation in this direction. His social history showed that as a matter of fact he was a laborer earning only a small wage; for years he had had difficulty in providing for his family, which included four children, and had been partially supported by charitable organizations.

An Austrian of about the same age, classified as having the same mental disease, also became maladjusted as a result of an exaggerated belief in himself. He was not talkative, but became greatly excited when displeased by anything. When asked about money, he answered very promptly that he had little, that he owned only a small store and was in debt for it, and was indifferent to suggestions regarding his future financial possibilities. He at once became very garrulous, however, when questioned about his accomplishments, stating that he had written hundreds of songs of the best kind which were played nightly in all the cafés of Vienna and broadcast from all the radio stations of the world. This man had been interested in intellectual and artistic pursuits, had attended opera and concerts frequently, and had dabbled in music for a time, learning to play the piano fairly well.

The effect of attitudes of inferiority, although illustrated best in abnormal individuals, can also be seen in the social behavior of the average person. When we attempt to reach a definite desired goal in life we usually assume characteristics which will help us to attain it.   A person who was treated unfairly during childhood and had no opportunity to express himself socially may become egocentric and overbearing as an adult.

Recent studies indicate that the appearance of reactions which characterize abnormal social behavior is often due to the attempt to adjust to the environment through newly assumed attitudes. A certain sequence in the development of the final abnormality is noted in all behavior disturbances. Conflict between the individual's wishes and existing conditions produces a change in attitude toward the particular situation which has aroused the difficulty.   Unbalance between behavior and the existing conditions results.   Abnormal emotional responses then develop because it becomes necessary to change emotional reactions when attitudes and behavior change.   The primary factor in the development of a social maladjustment is thus a change in attitudes; the individual then finds it necessary to justify his behavior and assumes responses at variance with those usually called normal.

The following case illustrates the way antisocial habits may be formed which interfere with a child's ability to coöperate in a social group.   A little girl of two and one-half is a problem in the nursery school because she is continually molesting other children.   When she sees a child with a toy she pushes or scratches him and takes his toy away, although at times she drops it as soon as she has obtained possession. Not only when she wishes to take something that belongs to another, but also on other occasions she suddenly runs up to a child and pushes, scratches or hits him, and then runs away. Her behavior, which is accompanied by every manifestation usually observed in anger, is clearly not due to a wish to defend herself or to get possession of a toy, for she reacts similarly toward objects in which she has no interest. The history of this girl indicates that her first playmates were smaller than she, and that her first objectionable behavior was a domination of younger children. She then developed habits which she transferred to a group her own age or older. Her reactions towards others' possessions in which she has no particular interest would indicate that much of her present aggressive behavior is due to the habits she formed at the earlier stage in her career.

Adults often assume characteristics which distinguish them as "different" or "worth noticing." Behavior of this type is repeated because of the favorable results obtained, and finally becomes habitual, although the individual may himself be unaware of its origin and development. He may be unwilling to analyze his reactions because unusual behavior is generally considered undesirable. But when others attach importance to it, this suggests to him that his conduct is striking and he has no desire to change it.

We have seen how adaptive behavior develops as a result of experience. Personality, then, which is made up of characteristic behavior, is especially fashioned by experience, for the process of human behavior is truly a developmental process of adaptation of the individual to his environment.

INDEX

Index